A World Directory
of
Theological Libraries

by

G. Martin Ruoss

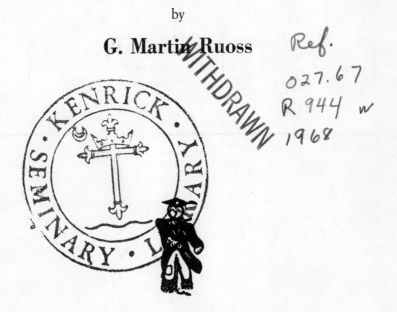

The Scarecrow Press, Inc.
Metuchen, N.J.   1968

Table of Contents

Introduction

The chance remark that "Chicago is the theological capital of the world" sired this report. While trying to learn whether or not Chicago is such a capital, I surveyed Jewish, Orthodox, Protestant and Roman Catholic sources as well as the standard published library directories and saw that no comprehensive directory of theological libraries of the world existed. I resolved to fill this gap.

A second reason for this venture is the frequent reporting in theological journals of seminary mergers, relocations and shared facilities. It is hoped that this directory will afford help to those who must study such events by providing an overview of the scheme of theological seminaries and libraries at the end of 1966.

A third factor, purely personal, was that in beginning a new professional position I wished to know about the wide range of theological seminaries and their libraries. The information was so diverse that a simple directory seemed a logical first step.

It was decided that theological seminaries and their libraries were to be noted as of December, 1966; accordingly, 1966 became the determinative year for this study. To aid in this goal a survey of current directories and subject guides to libraries was made.

A direct mailing, first class and air mail, was sent to those responsible for theological education in the various religious groups. The response was prompt--few complete lists of theological seminaries existed; however, such lists as did exist, as well as further sources of information, were graciously furnished and, in turn, were pursued by mail. Thus, one of the additional by-products of this study will be a reasonably comprehensive world directory of theological seminaries. The theological libraries listed as of November 10, 1967, totalled 1,778. There is almost an equal number of libraries containing theological materials in places classed as church libraries, monastic and cathedral libraries, abbeys, historical collections, archival depositories, museums and in-

5

stitutes. These have not been included in this report but could be a part of a second edition of this directory if that seems worthwhile.

It became apparent that some libraries were ancient while others were new. A form to be used to study such a variety would have to be readily understood by libarians who speak many different languages. Each institution was approached by direct mail--most by air mail. As of November 10, 1967, the cut-off date for incorporating replies into this report, 682 or 39% had replied. I wish to express gratitude to those librarians, principals, presidents, professors, tutors and others who took time to do another task and to do it well. The large number of personal letters and photographs attached to the replies is a sign of empathy in this project.

There is an imperative need for theological librarians to cooperate and share their insights and materials. I hope that as a result of this report librarians will "adopt" a library and a librarian in another land. This adopting could be in the form of willingness to share reports, letters, books, periodicals and other library materials on a regular basis. A more ecumenical approach, on two levels, is needed in this cooperative task: on the first level something newsy and folksy that involves librarians everywhere, such as the Ecumenical Press Service mimeo notes; on the second level a professional journal, not unlike UNESCO Bulletin for Libraries, which would be a means of assisting all seminaries and their theological libraries and librarians in the task at hand. The machinery for such communication is not difficult, but leadership to nourish and sustain it needs to be found.

In the section entitled "Interpretation of Reports," the study seeks to relate the specific to the general and to point out what are the most significant bits of information, as well as hinting at ideas for others to explore.

The compiler will be grateful for information about omissions and errors in this report. Hopefully, those who did not return the first questionnaire will eventually do so in order that their information may be included in a revised edition.

A special word of appreciation is due the Theological Education Fund, whose staff provided encouragement, reports, lists and opportunities to check their files for additional information. Their pioneer work in gathering such information is noteworthy, and their ecumenical reporting is unique.

This World Directory of Theological Libraries lists
libraries which exist to help persons prepare for the rabbin-
ate, the Christian ministry and the priesthood. I have included some libraries which, in another country, might be
deemed sub-standard, or which might be considered inappro-
priate by another sponsoring religious group, and have at-
tempted to record all graduate theological libraries as well
as all academic establishments that qualify individuals to be
"set apart" for full-time work in synagogue or church.

A word of comfort to my wife for her attention to de-
tail and care in typing; she may now anticipate sharing a few
library holidays in other pursuits.

November 10, 1967   G. Martin Ruoss

Interpretation of the Reports

What's in the Name?

In choosing a name for a theological educational institution, neither geography, history, ecclesiastical or religious maturity, nor the size of the sponsoring body seems to have any distinctive value. The adjective Christian is infrequently used in this connection.

The nomenclature chart identifies the names of theological institutions, the number of times they occur and the rank by frequency.

Nomenclature Chart

Name	Number	Rank
Abbey	17	10
Academy of Theology	6	
Athenaeum	6	
Bible College	4	
Bible School	6	
Bible Seminary	5	
Biblical Seminary	5	
Center	6	
Center of Theological Studies	1	
Christian Academy	1	
College	180	3
College of Divinity	2	
College of Theology	3	
Department for the Study of Religion	1	
Department of Christian Studies	1	
Department of Religious Studies	2	
Department of Theology	3	
Divinity College	1	
Divinity Department	1	
Divinity Faculty	1	
Divinity House	2	
Divinity School	20	9

9

Name	Number	Rank
Division of Religion and Philosophy	1	
Ecclesiastical School	1	
Faculty of Divinity	2	
Faculty of Humanities	1	
Faculty of Jewish Studies	1	
Faculty of Religion	2	
Faculty of Theological Science	1	
Faculty of Theology	90	5
Graduate Seminary	1	
Hall	8	
Hebrew Union College and Jewish Institute of Religion	6	
House	10	
House and Center	1	
House of Israel	1	
House of Studies	9	
Institute	81	7
Institute of Philosophy and Religion	7	
Institute of Theology	3	
Mission	4	
Monastery	8	
Oratory	1	
Ordination College	1	
Ordination House	1	
Pastor's College	2	
Pastor's School	8	
Preparatory	1	
Priory	1	
Rabbinical College	2	
Scholasticate	9	
School	4	
School for the Ministry	1	
School of Christian Education	1	
School of Divinity	1	
School of Religion	7	
School of the Bible	1	
School of Theology	37	8
Seminary	715	1
Seminary Foundation	1	
Talmudical Academy	1	
Talmudical College	1	
Theologate	1	
Theological Academy	1	
Theological Center	1	
Theological College	86	6
Theological Department	4	

Theological Faculty	9	
Theological Institute	12	
Theological School	22	
Theological Seminary	186	2
Theological Training Program	1	
Theological Training School	2	
Theological Union	1	
Theologisches Hochschule	13	
Training College	10	
Training School	5	
Yeshiva Torah Vodaoth	1	
Non-descriptive	125	4

The use of the most popular names is reported as follows:
    Theology: 20 names--483 institutions
    Seminary: 6 names--910 institutions
    College: 12 names--299 institutions
    School: 13 names--114 institutions
    Faculty: 7 names--106 institutions

The report also indicates that seminaries are named predominantly for the place and least of all for Biblical characters.

Named after geographic places	761
Named after historic persons (Wesley, Pius XI, Augustine, St. Chad, etc.)	361
Named after religious designations (Friends, Lutheran, Baptist, etc.)	160
Named after ideas (Sacred Heart, Holy Trinity, House of Mission, etc.)	151
Named after Biblical persons (St. Paul, St. John, Mary, etc.)	132

Many names include more than one of these designations.

Geographical Summaries and Concentrations

A count of the listings reveals that theological libraries are divided almost equally between the Eastern and Western Hemispheres. There is a predominance of Protestant seminaries and libraries in Africa, Asia and Oceania, following the missionary movements of the past centuries.

Reflection on the geographic distribution points to common ventures in theological libraries in Central and South America as a most fruitful place to begin.

Italy is the country with the greatest number of theological seminaries and libraries; and Washington, D.C., U.S.A., is the city that has more theological libraries than any other place on the globe. The following cities--not metropolitan areas--report more than ten theological institutions and libraries:

Berlin, Germany
Boston, Massachusetts, U.S.A.
Buenos Aires, Argentina
Capetown, Rep. of South Africa
Chicago, Illinois, U.S.A.
Hong Kong, N.T.
Jerusalem, Israel
London, England
Manila, The Philippines
Melbourne, Victoria, Australia
Mexico City, Mexico
Montreal, Quebec, Canada
New York, New York, U.S.A.
Paris, France
Rome, Italy
Sao Paulo, Brazil
Seoul, Korea
Tokyo, Japan
Toronto, Ontario, Canada
Washington, D.C., U.S.A. (greatest number)

Of these concentrations, there are six in North America, five in Asia, four in Europe, two in South America, one in Africa, one in Central America and one in Oceania.

In addition to these twenty clusters of theological seminaries, the following areas have five or more institutions: Atlanta, Georgia, U.S.A.; Amsterdam, Netherlands; Barcelona, Spain; Berkeley, California, U.S.A.; Budapest, Hungary; Dubuque, Iowa, U.S.A.; Geneva, Switzerland; Minneapolis-St. Paul, Minnesota, U.S.A.; Ottawa, Canada; Oxford, England; Philadelphia, Pennsylvania, U.S.A.; Porto Alegre, Brazil; St. Louis, Missouri, U.S.A.; and Taipei, Taiwan.

Geographic Areas with Number
of Theological Libraries

Summary of Countries

Africa		36
Asia		22
Canada (8 provinces)		1
Caribbean		8
Central America		8
Europe		30
Oceania		18
Melanesia	5	
Micronesia	1	
Polynesia	4	
Australia	6	
New Zealand	1	
Tasmania	1	
South America		11
U.S.A. (47 states)		1
	Total	135

Rank by Geographic Area and % of Total

Europe	658	37%
U.S.A.	377	21%
Asia	232	13%
Africa	174	10%
South America	138	8%
Canada	70	4%
Central America	52	3%
Oceania	50	3%
Caribbean	27	1%

Specific Countries with Number
of Theological Libraries

Africa

Algeria	2
Angola	4
Burundi	2
Cameroon, Federal Republic of	6
Cape Verde Islands	1
Central African Republic	1
Congo, Republic of	4
Congo, Democratic Republic of	18
Dahomey	2
Ethiopia	6

Africa (cont.)

Fernando Po	1
Ghana	6
Ivory Coast, Republic of	1
Kenya	7
Lesotho	3
Liberia	2
Malagasy Republic	10
Malawi	2
Mauritania, Islamic Republic of	1
Mozambique	7
Nigeria, Federal Republic of	14
Nyassaland	1
Portuguese East Africa	1
Rhodesia	7
Rwanda	1
Senegal	1
Sierra Leone	2
South Africa, Republic of	28
South West Africa	2
Sudan, Republic of	2
Tanzania, United Republic of	10
Tunisia	2
Uganda	8
United Arab Republic	5
Upper Volta	1
Zambia, Republic of	3

Asia

Burma	8
Ceylon	6
Hong Kong	10
India	51
Indonesia	20
Iran	1
Iraq	2
Israel	11
Japan	28
Jordan	1
Korea	25
Lebanon	12
Macao	1
Malaysia, Federation of	4
Pakistan	3
Philippines, The	19
Singapore	2
South Vietnam	9

Taiwan   14
Thailand   2
Turkey   3

Caribbean

Bahamas   1
Barbados   1
Cuba   4
Dominican Republic   2
Haiti   3
Jamaica   6
Puerto Rico   6
Trinidad   4

Central America

British Honduras   1
Costa Rica   5
El Salvador   2
Guatemala   6
Honduras   3
Mexico   31
Nicaragua   3
Panama   1

Europe

Austria   11
Belgium   16
Bulgaria   3
Czechoslovakia   3
Denmark   6
England   59
Finland   3
France   111
Germany, Democratic Republic   19
Germany, Federal Republic   57
Greece   5
Hungary   8
Iceland   1
Ireland   14
Italy   131
Luxembourg   1
Malta   3
Netherlands   25
Norway   2
Poland   28
Portugal   14

Europe (cont.)

Rumania	11
Russia	7
Scotland	9
Spain	69
Sweden	3
Switzerland	20
Wales	8
Yugoslavia	11

North America--Canada

Alberta	2
British Columbia	2
Manitoba	1
Newfoundland	1
Nova Scotia	5
Ontario	26
Quebec	30
Saskatchewan	3

North America--U.S.A.

Alabama	1
Arkansas	3
Arizona	2
California	33
Colorado	4
Connecticut	8
District of Columbia	30
Florida	3
Georgia	5
Illinois	29
Indiana	13
Iowa	7
Kansas	2
Kentucky	8
Louisiana	3
Maine	1
Maryland	11
Massachusetts	21
Michigan	6
Minnesota	10
Mississippi	2
Missouri	17
Nebraska	1
New Hampshire	2
New Jersey	9
New Mexico	1

New York	32
North Carolina	6
Ohio	22
Oklahoma	2
Oregon	4
Pennsylvania	26
Rhode Island	1
South Carolina	8
South Dakota	3
Tennessee	6
Texas	15
Utah	1
Vermont	1
Virginia	6
Washington	2
Wisconsin	10

Oceania

Australia	
Australian Capital Territory	1
New South Wales	6
Queensland	4
South Australia	3
Victoria	10
West Australia	1
Melanesia	
Fiji Islands	4
New Caledonia	2
New Guinea	5
New Hebrides	1
Solomon Islands	1
Micronesia	
Gilbert Islands	1
New Zealand	5
Polynesia	
Cook Islands	1
Samoa	2
Tahiti	1
Tonga	1
Tasmania	1

South America

Argentina	26
Bolivia	9
Brazil	48
Chile	8
Colombia	19

South America (cont.)
Ecuador	3
Paraguay	5
Peru	11
Surinam	1
Uruguay	3
Venezuela	5

Denominational Descriptions

There are eighty groups represented in this index.
This number does not include the non-denominational or independent and private institutions. Those with a larger than average number of institutions are:

Roman Catholic	890	Methodist	81
Anglican	133	Presbyterian	69
Baptist	118	Orthodox	48
Lutheran	83	Reformed	40

The following charts indicate the worldwide locations of the major groups:

Geographic Distribution of Theological Seminaries and Libraries

Area	Total	Prot.	R.C.	Orth.	Jewish	Other
Africa	174	112	48	4	0	10
Asia	232	139	59	8	5	21
Canada	70	26	44	0	0	0
Caribbean	27	20	6	0	0	1
Central America	52	25	27	0	0	0
Europe	658	120	457	26	8	47
Oceania	50	38	8	0	1	3
South America	138	66	69	0	1	2
U.S.A.	377	164	172	7	16	18

Rank by Religious Group in Geographic Area

Protestant

U.S.A.	164	Oceania	38
Asia	139	Canada	26
Europe	120	Central America	25
Africa	112	Caribbean	20
South America	66		

Roman Catholic		Jewish	
Europe	457	U.S.A.	16
U.S.A.	172	Europe	8
South America	69	Asia	5
Asia	59	South America	1
Africa	48	Oceania	1
Canada	44		
Central America	27	Other	
Oceania	8	Europe	47
Caribbean	6	Asia	21
		U.S.A.	18
Orthodox		Africa	10
Europe	26	Oceania	3
Asia	8	South America	2
U.S.A.	7	Caribbean	1
Africa	4		

Library Chronology

These observations and dates are only about the theological libraries reporting and do not pertain to the supporting institutions.

Number of Theological Libraries Established, by Centuries

600 A.D.	1
900	1
1400	3
1500	8
1600	15
1700	13
1800	183
1900	371

Chart of Dates and Number of Theological Libraries Established Each Year

635	1	1559	1	1615	1	1673	1
952	1	1562	1	1637	1	1680	1
1400	1	1563	1	1650	2	1692	1
1495	1	1576	1	1654	1	1700	1
1498	1	1577	1	1660	1	1711	1
1527	1	1600	1	1666	1	1726	1
1544	1	1609	1	1668	1	1732	1
1558	1	1611	1	1669	1	1735	1

Chart of Dates and Number of Theological
Libraries Established (cont.)

1737	1	1854	2	1906	2	1952	11
1751	1	1855	2	1907	4	1953	11
1757	1	1856	2	1908	1	1954	10
1759	1	1857	1	1909	5	1955	8
1773	1	1858	2	1910	7	1956	9
1778	1	1859	4	1911	3	1957	15
1784	1	1860	3	1912	5	1958	14
1794	1	1861	1	1913	3	1959	2
1800	3	1862	1	1914	4	1960	17
1802	1	1863	2	1915	3	1961	8
1803	1	1864	2	1916	2	1962	12
1804	1	1865	2	1917	4	1963	1
1805	2	1866	4	1918	2	1964	8
1806	1	1867	6	1920	3	1965	9
1807	2	1869	4	1921	3	1966	4
1808	2	1871	3	1922	6	1967	2
1809	1	1873	3	1923	3	1968	1
1810	2	1875	9	1924	11		
1812	2	1876	4	1925	5		
1815	1	1877	1	1926	3		
1817	3	1878	4	1927	7		
1818	2	1879	1	1928	2		
1820	1	1880	3	1929	4		
1823	2	1881	3	1930	5		
1824	1	1883	1	1931	2		
1825	2	1884	2	1932	10		
1826	1	1885	1	1933	2		
1827	1	1887	1	1934	3		
1828	1	1888	1	1935	4		
1829	1	1889	4	1936	3		
1830	2	1890	5	1937	3		
1831	2	1891	3	1938	4		
1834	3	1892	5	1939	5		
1836	1	1893	4	1940	6		
1839	3	1894	1	1941	4		
1840	1	1895	3	1942	4		
1841	2	1896	3	1943	1		
1842	3	1897	4	1944	4		
1845	1	1898	6	1945	2		
1846	2	1899	2	1946	8		
1847	2	1900	2	1947	12		
1849	1	1901	4	1948	9		
1850	3	1903	5	1949	8		
1852	5	1904	3	1950	14		
1853	3	1905	6	1951	5		

The year 1960 saw the greatest number of new theological libraries established. From the start of World War
II in 1942 to the end of 1966, 208 were founded. Since 1800,
there are ony 25 years in which a new theological library was
not begun; in the twentieth century the only blank years are
1902 and 1919! In a very few instances the actual date of
a library's founding is unknown.

Date of Establishment of
Earliest Theological Library Still
in Use in Each Area

635 A. D.	Europe	The Dean and Chapter Library, Durham, England
952 A. D.	Africa	The Library of the Greek Orthodox Patriarchate of Alexandria and All Egypt
1554	South America	Pontificial y Civil Facultad de Teologia, Lima, Peru
1611	Asia	University of Santo Tomas Library, Manila, The Philippines
1789	Canada	University of King's College Library, Halifax, Nova Scotia
1807	U. S. A.	Andover Newton Theological School--Hills Library, Newton Centre, Massachusetts
1830	Caribbean	Codrington College Library, St. John, Barbados
1834	Oceania	St. Patrick's Ecclesiastical College Library, Manly, New South Wales, Australia
1855	Central America	Biblioteca del Seminario Conciliar de San Luis Potosi, Mexico

Architectural Achievements

The library building is of all kinds, shapes, designs,
conversions, adaptations and modifications. Classrooms,
old houses, halls, basements and administrative space ap-
pear to offer readiest use for the library. One report indicates use of a converted chapel, another an old bar, another
a dining room, another an "ancient room." There are many excellent new and modern buildings. There is a wide diversity of
style in the library buildings of each geographic area. From
the notes on the reports, it is evident that in coming years many
new library buildings will be erected and many others will need

to expand.

The architectural needs of the library are further re-
vealed in the statistics on utilization of library buildings.
Of the reporting institutions, 442 or 68% indicated that their
building was used solely for library purposes; 468 or 73%
said that open stacks are the custom. Relative to capacity,
80 are full or overflowing. Examples are the Chung Chi
College Library in Hong Kong with 84,645 volumes in space
designed for 50,000; and the Ecole Unie de Theologie in Luluabourg, Democratic Republic of the Congo, with 4,500
books in space provided for 1,500.

The Heroic Few--Theological Librarians

It is significant that 10% of the theological libraries
reporting have no designated professional librarian or staff,
and that 40% operate with a single staff person.   Only 20%
have more than one professional librarian.

Number of Professional Librarians	Number of Institutions
1	237
2	121
3	60
4	35
5	14
6	16
7	9
8	7
9	1
10	2
10+	14
None	86

The Common Theological Languages

It was assumed that theological libraries would use
the language of their country; it was unexpected to discover
that English ranks as the predominant language in more than
80% of the reporting libraries. The other dominant languages
in order of numerical frequency are French, German and
Spanish.

Predominant Language	Number of Libraries
English	277
French	37
German	25
Spanish	23
Latin	4
Portuguese	4
Hebrew	3
Armenian	2
Dutch	1
Greek	1
Hungarian	1
Korean	1
Multi-lingual	173

The Amazing Book Holdings

A thrilling story is told of books held for use in theological seminaries. From the smallest (The Han Yang Theological Seminary Library of Seoul, Korea, with 80 volumes) to the largest (Bibliothèque Institut Catholique de Paris with 600,000 volumes), there is an amazing wealth of resources available for theological study. These few observations indicate the significance:

North America has the fewest number of libraries
    with less than 25,000 volumes.
North America has as many libraries with more than
    25,000 volumes as the rest of the world.
Only 54 libraries report holdings of more than
    100,000 volumes.
The median for all reporting libraries lies between
    15,000 and 20,000 volumes.

Number of Volumes Held by Reporting Libraries at End of 1966

Volumes	Libraries	Volumes	Libraries
0-500	9	4,001-5,000	16
501-1,000	12	5,001-6,000	24
1,001-1,500	16	6,001-7,000	26
1,501-2,000	10	7,001-8,000	15
2,001-2,500	17	8,001-9,000	14
2,501-3,000	7	9,001-10,000	4
3,001-4,000	30	10,001-15,000	65

Volumes	Libraries	Volumes	Libraries
15,001-20,000	40	90,001-100,000	14
20,001-25,000	44	100,001-125,000	14
25,001-30,000	38	125,001-150,000	10
30,001-35,000	18	150,001-175,000	4
35,001-40,000	22	175,001-200,000	5
40,001-50,000	10	200,001-250,000	7
50,001-60,000	26	250,001-300,000	6
60,001-70,000	21	300,001-400,000	6
70,001-80,000	19	400,001-500,000	0
80,001-90,000	16	500,001-600,000	2

Classification Schemes Run On and On

The following table reveals that Dewey is the most common classification system, although used by less than half of the reporting institutions. There are 37 different systems in use. If the 74 schemes that are noted as "own" are added to these 37, the total is 111--a fantastic array! The system chosen for classifying the books in a particular library appears to depend on the missionary experience of the church and on the level of library work locally available.

Classification Scheme	Number of Libraries
Dewey	240
Library of Congress	93
Own	74
Combinations	57
Union Theological Seminary	47
Subject	21
A-Z	18
None	12
Universal Decimal	9
Accession	9
Decimal	8
Authors	5
Cutter	5
Size	5
Card	4
Nippon Decimal	4
Fixed Location	3
International Card	3
Vatican	3
Bliss	2
Freidus	2

Classification Scheme	Number of Libraries
Memory-o-matic	2
Numerical	2
Westminster (Philadelphia)	2

The following classification systems are reported in use by only one library: Alpha-numeric, Blackwell's Theological Catalog, British Museum Modified, C.D.V., Classic, Eppelsheim, French, Korean Decimal, New York Public Library, Old French, Pierce, Staatsbibliotek (Munich), Union (Jerusalem), Union (St. John's), Yale and Language.

Faculty-Student Use of the Library

Restrictive use is common in theological libraries in all countries and by all religious groups. The founding dates of the reporting libraries seem to indicate that it is a matter of policy rather than a trend.

Only faculty-student use was reported by 282 libraries or 49%, while unrestricted use was reported by 296 libraries or 51%. Of the latter, the greatest number were in Europe and the greatest percentage was in Central America.

Special Collections

Less than half of the reporting libraries have special collections. The greatest number, as well as the greatest percentage, are in the U.S.A. It is hoped that, as a result of this directory, a detailed exploration of these special collections will be made.

Special Collections in Reporting Libraries

Geographic Area	Yes	No
U.S.A.	115	85
Europe	75	69
Asia	22	60
Africa	12	33
Canada	11	19
South America	11	30
Oceania	8	10
Central America	4	10
Totals	259	323

Periodicals

Although periodicals are meant to keep the channels of theological communication open, it is surprising how insignificant they are in these reports. All but two libraries report that they receive periodicals, but the spectrum is wide between those receiving but a single subscription and the Bibliotheca Pontificii Athenaei Antoniani Faculty of Theology in the Vatican City reporting 2,505. Several universities reported a larger number of subscriptions, but they were not restricted to the theological area. The median number of subscriptions is 40. This table illustrates the median for the various geographic areas:

Periodical Subscriptions

Area	Median
Africa	10
Asia	40
Canada	90
Caribbean	10
Central America	10
Europe	50
Oceania	10
South America	20
U.S.A.	200

Number of Periodical Subscriptions and Percentage Bound

Number of Periodical Subscriptions	Number of Libraries	Percentage of Periodicals Bound	Number of Libraries
0	2	None	91
1-10	57	10%	34
11-100	331	20%	25
101-200	91	30%	22
201-300	53	40%	26
301-400	37	50%	44
401-500	23	60%	21
501-600	13	70%	33
601-700	9	80%	66
701-800	7	90%	44
801-900	2	100%	45
901-1,000	2		
Over 1,000	10		

The question arises as to whether the exchange of periodicals between libraries, as currently practiced through the American Theological Library Association, would be beneficial on a worldwide scale, or whether it would be better for institutions "adopting" another library to express their concern by taking periodical subscriptions in their names.

Diverse Library Materials

Perhaps the pertinent question is, "How useful or important to theological libraries are these items?"

Items Owned	Number of Libraries
Maps	219
Archives	182
Microforms	176
Vertical Files	174
Slides	165
Music	144
Flat Pictures	129
Films	79

It is noteworthy that only eleven libraries report owning all eight of these varied auxiliary library materials.

Further studies concerning the archival holdings of theological libraries and the practicability of "interlibrary loan" of these eight items would prove valuable.

Professional Memberships

Roman Catholic, Jewish and all Protestant groups need the exchange of practices and the cooperation that professional associations afford. The American Theological Library Association (ATLA), by virtue of its excellent purpose, should become an effective international organization. One way of bringing this about would be for each current ATLA member to sponsor a librarian from another country or from another religious group.

Membership in Professional Organizations	Number of Librarians
National and International	123
ATLA	117
State and Regional	99
Religious	78
Other	46
None	298

Explanation of Entries

The order is geographic by continents, countries, provinces or states, cities and institutions. This order affords users a quick visualization of the strength or weakness of theological education in a particular area. The information given is as described by the institutions. Accent marks are omitted in foreign names and titles.

Abbreviations Used

Information Sequence

Part I
Name and address of institution
Supporting body (in parentheses)
Date of institution's founding

Part II
Library (including unique name)
Date of library's founding
Number of staff members
Separate library building

OB
OS

Open stacks
Book capacity - Current holdings
Predominant language

D	Dutch
E	English
F	French
G	German
I	Italian
J	Japanese
L	Latin
P	Portuguese
S	Spanish

Classification system

DDC	Dewey
KDC	Korean
LC	Library of Congress

29

Abbreviations Used		Information Sequence
NYPL	New York Public Library	
NDC	Nippon	
UTS	Union Theological Seminary	
UDC	Universal Decimal	
F-S		Faculty-Student use only
SC		Special collections
		Periodicals received - Bound
Ar		Archives
Fi		Films
Sl		Slides
Mi		Microforms
Pi		Flat pictures
Ma		Maps
Mu		Music
VF		Vertical file

Sample Entry

CALIFORNIA BAPTIST THEOLOGICAL SEMINARY. Seminary Knolls, Covina, California 91722 U.S.A. (American
Baptist Convention) 1944.
Library: 1946, 1+, OB, OS, 63,000-55,090, E F G, DDC,
678-650, Ar Sl Mi Pi Ma Mu VF

Part II of the sample entry gives the following information: The California Baptist Theological Seminary Library
was founded in 1946 and has a staff of 1+; has a separate
library building, open stacks, a book capacity of 63,000 and
holdings as of December, 1966, of 55,090; English, French,
and German are the predominant languages; books are classed
according to the Dewey Decimal Classification; 678 periodicals are received, 650 periodicals are bound; they have ar-
chives, slides, microforms, flat pictures, maps, music and
a vertical file. Since they do not limit their services to
faculty-student use and since they have no special collections
or films, the symbols for these are omitted from the entry.

Alphabetic List of Abbreviations

Ar	Archives
D	Dutch
DDC	Dewey Decimal Classification
E	English
F	French
F-S	Faculty-Student Use Only
Fi	Films
G	German
I	Italian
J	Japanese
KDC	Korean Decimal Classification
L	Latin
LC	Library of Congress
Ma	Maps
Mi	Microforms
Mu	Music
NDC	Nippon Decimal Classification
NYPL	New York Public Library
OB	Separate Library Building
OS	Open Stacks
P	Portuguese
Pi	Pictures
S	Spanish
SC	Special Collections
Sl	Slides
UDC	Universal Decimal Classification
UTS	Union Theological Seminary (N. Y.)
VF	Vertical File

A few abbreviations used by reporting libraries could not be verified.

Geographic Index of Theological
Seminaries and Libraries

Africa

Cameroon (cont.)
 4011, Yaounde, Cameroon (West African churches:
 Presbyterian, Methodist, Evangelical, etc.) 1960.
 Library: 1960, 1, OB, OS, 20,000-7,000, F, UDC,
 F-S, SC, 150-___, Ar Mi Ma VF   13
THEOLOGICAL COLLEGE OF THE PRESBYTERIAN
 CHURCH IN WEST CAMEROON. Nyasoso via Kumba,
 West Cameroon (Presbyterian Church in West Came-
 roon) 1952.
 Library: 1952, 1, OB, OS, 4,000-2,310, E, DDC,
 F-S, 40-40, Fi Sl Mi Pi Ma VF   14

Cape Verde Islands
SEMINARIO NAZARENO. Apartado 8, Mindelo, S. Vin-
 cente, Cape Verde Islands (Church of the Nazarene)
 1952.   15

Central African Republic
ECOLE DE THEOLOGIE. B. P. 37, Carnot, Central
 African Republic (Union of Baptist Churches of the
 West) 1953.   16

Congo, Democratic Republic of the
GRAND SEMINAIRE "ST. THOMAS." Baudouinville,
 Dem. Rep. of the Congo (Roman Catholic).   17
ECOLE DE THEOLOGIE AU CONGO DU NORD. A. I. M.
 Linga, B. P. 143, Bunia, Dem. Rep. of the Congo
 (Africa Inland Mission, Unevangelized Fields Mission)
 1961.   18
GRAND SEMINAIRE "ST. PIERRE CLAVER." Burasira-
 Usumbura (Urundi) Dem. Rep. of the Congo (Roman
 Catholic).   19
ECOLE DE PASTEURS ET D'INSTITUTEURS. E. P. I.,
 Kimpese, Kinshasa, Dem. Rep. of the Congo (Churches
 founded by four American, British and Swedish Mis-
 sions) 1908.
 Library: 1908, 2, OB, OS, 20,000-7,000, F E, DDC,
 F-S, SC, 35-0   20
ECOLE DE THEOLOGIE. A. M. Z. M. - C. T. M., B. P.
 4081, Kinshasa II, Dem. Rep. of the Congo (Congo
 Inland Mission and American Mennonite Brethren Mis-
 sion) 1964.
 Library: 1964, 1, OS, 2,000-800, F, DDC, F-S,
 10-0, Sl   21
ECOLE MOYENNE PASTORALE. A. B. F. M. S., A. P.
 4728, Kinshasa, Dem. Rep. of the Congo (American
 Baptist Foreign Mission Society) 1950.

Library: 1950, 1, OS, 1,500-471, F, own, F-S,
2-0, Sl Ma   22
FACULTE DE THEOLOGIE PROTESTANTE AU CONGO.
B. P. 4369, Kinshasa, Dem. Rep. of the Congo
(Baptist, Disciples, Methodist, Presbyterian) 1960.   23
SALVATION ARMY TRAINING SCHOOL. Armse du
Salut, B. P. 8803, Kinshasa, Dem. Rep. of the
Congo (Salvation Army) 1938.   24
UNIVERSITE LOUVANIUM DE LEOPOLDVILLE,
FACULTY OF THEOLOGY. P.O. Box 121, Kin-
shasa, Dem. Rep. of the Congo (Roman Catholic)
1947.   25
ECOLE DE PREDICATEURS. E. P. C. Luebo, B. P.
117, Luluabourg, Dem. Rep. of the Congo (Eglise
Presbyterienne au Congo) 1958.
Library: 1958, 2, OB, OS   26
ECOLE UNIE DE THEOLOGIE. B. P. 159, Luluabourg,
Dem. Rep. of the Congo (Eglise du Christ au Congo,
Disciples du Christ--United Christian Missionary So-
ciety, Eglise Presbyterienne au Congo--Board of
World Missions, Presbyterian U. S., Eglise Presby-
terienne au Ruanda--Mission Evangelique de Belgique)
1961.
Library: 1961, 0, OB, OS, 1,500-4,500, E F, DDC,
F-S, SC, 25-1, Ma Mu   27
GRAND SEMINAIRE "CHRIST ROI." Kabwe, Luluabourg,
Dem. Rep. of the Congo (Roman Catholic).   28
GRAND SEMINAIRE "ST. ROBERT BELLARIUM."
Mayidi-Kisanter, Mayidi, Dem. Rep. of the Congo
(Roman Catholic).   29
KAYEKA-KIMBULU ECOLE DE THEOLOGIE UNIE.
Mulungwishi sac prive via Elizabethville, Dem. Rep.
of the Congo (Methodist) 1951.   30
GRAND SEMINAIRE "ST. ALBERT-LE-GRAND." Nangara,
Dem. Rep. of the Congo (Roman Catholic).   31
GRAND SEMINAIRE "ST. CHARLES." Nyakibanda par
Astride (Ruanda), Nyakibanda, Dem. Rep. of the
Congo (Roman Catholic).   32
INSTITUT BIBLIQUE. (E.B.B.F.), B. F. 107, Thys-
ville, Dem. Rep. of the Congo (Baptist Churches of
the Congo) 1964.   33
INSTITUT BIBLIQUE. B. P. 1, Tshikapa, Dem. Rep.
of the Congo (Congo Inland Mission--Mennonite) 1953. 34

Republic of Congo
GRAND SEMINAIRE. Brazzaville, Republic of Congo
(Roman Catholic).   35

Republic of Congo (cont.)
SEMINAIRE EVANGELIQUE DE NGUEDI.   B. P. 8,
   Nguedi, Lutete, Brazzaville, Republic of Congo
   (Reformed, Evangelical Church of the Congo) 1931.   36
INSTITUT BIBLIQUE DE L'UBANGI.   B. P. 140, Genena,
   Republic of Congo (Evangelical Free Church, Evangel-
   ical Covenant Church, Church of Christ in Uganda)
   1948.   37
UNIVERSITE LIBRE DU CONGO--FACULTE DE
   THEOLOGIE. B. P. 2012, Kisangani, Republic of
   Congo (Conseil Protestant du Congo) 1963.
   Library: 1963, 1, OB, OS, 20,000-1,000, E, DDC,
   F-S   38

Dahomey
GRAND SEMINAIRE.   Ouidah, Dahomey (Roman Catho-
   lic).   39
ECOLE PASTORALE EVANGELIQUE.   B. P. 176,
   Porto Novo, Dahomey (Methodist, Reformed) 1962.   40

Ethiopia
HAILE SELASSIE I UNIVERSITY--THEOLOGICAL COL-
   LEGE OF THE HOLY TRINITY.   Addis Ababa,
   Ethiopia, 1961.   41
MEKANE JESUS SEMINARY.   P. O. Box 1247, Addis
   Ababa, Ethiopia (Lutheran: American, Swedish,
   German) 1960.   42
THEOLOGICAL COLLEGE OF THE HOLY TRINITY.
   P. O. Box 665, Addis Ababa, Ethiopia (Eastern
   Orthodox Church, Government) 1960.   43
MAJOR SEMINARY.   Adigrat, Ethiopia (Roman Catho-
   lic).   44
MAJOR SEMINARY.   Asmara, Ethiopia (Roman Catho-
   lic).   45
TABOR SEMINARY, NORWEGIAN LUTHERAN MISSION.
   Dilla, Ethiopia, 1952, 1956.
   Library: 1952, 1, OB, 600-600, E, subject, F-S,
   3-0   46

Fernando Po
SEMINARIO INDIGENO DEL PILAR.   Banapa, Fernando
   Po (Roman Catholic).   47

Ghana
GHANA BAPTIST SEMINARY.   P. O. Box 1,
   Abuakwa via Kumasi, Ghana (Ghana Baptist Mission
   of the Southern Baptist Convention) 1960.

Library: 1960, 0, OB, OS, 10,000-3,050, DDC,
F-S, 15-1, Pi Ma   48
ST. THERESA MAJOR SEMINARY. P.O. Box 27,
Cape Coast, Elmina, Ghana (Roman Catholic).   49
TRINITY COLLEGE. P.O. Box 413, Kumasi, Ghana
(Methodist, Presbyterian) 1943.   50
UNIVERSITY OF GHANA--DEPARTMENT FOR STUDY
OF RELIGION. Legon, Ghana (Government) 1948.   51
BAPTIST PASTOR'S SCHOOL. Box 78, Tamale, Ghana
(Ghana Baptists, Southern Baptists) 1960.   52
ST. CHARLES MAJOR SEMINARY. P.O. Box 42, Ta-
male, Ghana (Roman Catholic).   53

Ivory Coast
GRAND SEMINAIRE. Anyama par Abidijan, Anyama,
Ivory Coast (Roman Catholic).   54

Kenya
ST. NICHOLAS THEOLOGICAL SEMINARY. Waithaka,
P.O. Box 44, Kikuiu, Kenya (Orthodox Patriarchate
of Alexandria).   55
ST. PAUL'S UNITED THEOLOGICAL COLLEGE. P.O.
Limuru, Kenya (Anglican, Methodist, Presbyterian)
1903.
Library: 1950, 0, OB, OS, 9,000-6,000, E, DDC,
F-S, 20-0, Ma   56
SCOTT THEOLOGICAL COLLEGE. Box 49, Machakos,
Kenya (Africa Inland Mission) 1962.
Library: 1962, 1, OS, 3,500-3,500, E, DDC, F-S,
40-0, Ar Sl Ma VF   57
KIMA THEOLOGICAL COLLEGE. Box 75, Masena,
Kenya (Church of God Mission, Kima, Kenya) 1954.
Library: 1954, 1, OB, OS, 3,000-2,200, E, UTS,
F-S, 20-0, Sl Mu   58
OFFICERS TRAINING COLLEGE. P.O. Box 575,
Nairobi, Kenya (Salvation Army) 1931.   59
TRINITY COLLEGE. P.O. Box 12430, Nairobi, Kenya
(Anglican Church of the Province of East Africa)
1963.
Library: 1963, 0, OS, 2,000-1,300, E Swahili, DDC,
Ar Mu   60
ST. PAUL SEMINARY. P.O. Box 25, Nyeri, Kenya
(Roman Catholic).   61

Lesotho
MARIJA THEOLOGICAL COLLEGE. P.O. Box 32,
Marija, Lesotho (Presbyterian, Reformed) 1882.   62

Lesotho (cont.)
ST. AUGUSTINE'S SEMINARY. P.O. Roma, Lesotho
(Roman Catholic) 1924.
Library: 1953, 3, OS, 15,000-7,903, E, DDC, SC,
82-82   63
UNIVERSITY OF BASUTOLAND, BECHUANALAND
AND SWAZILAND--DEPARTMENT OF THEOLOGY.
Roma via Maseru, Lesotho (Roman Catholic, Govern-
ment) 1945.   64

Liberia
CUTTINGTON COLLEGE. c/o Bishop's House, Mon-
rovia, Liberia (Lutheran Church in America, Protes-
tant Episcopal Church of U.S.A.) 1941.
Library: 1949, 2, OB, OS, 80,000-___, E, LC,
SC, 257-___, Mi VF   65
LUTHERAN TRAINING INSTITUTE. Lutheran Mission,
P.O. Box 1046, Monrovia, Liberia (Lutheran)
1946.   66

Malagasy Republic
KOLEJIN'I SANTA PAOLY. Ambatoharanana, Meri-
mandroso, Ambohidratrimo, Malagasy Republic
(Diocese of Madagascar--Anglican Church) 1878.
Library: 1878, 1, OS, ___-1,800, F Malagasy,
F-S, 6-0, Pi Ma   67
SEKOLY PASTORAL. F.P.M., Ambotomanga par
Manyakandriana TCE, Malagasy Republic (Reformed)
1902.   68
IVATO UNITED THEOLOGICAL COLLEGE. Antananar-
ivo, Malagasy Republic (Union Board: Congregation-
al, Reformed, Society of Friends, Union Church of
North Madagascar) 1966.   69
KOLEJIN'I FRENJY. Tsarabonenana, Arivonimorno,
Malagasy Republic (Society of Friends) 1936.   70
COLLEGE PASTORAL. F.K.M., Amboniavaratra,
Fianarantsoa, Malagasy Republic (The Church of
Christ in Madagascar--Eto Madagasikara) 1876.
Library: 1876, 0, OB, OS, 5,000-550, E F Mala-
gasy, F-S, 4-0, Ar Pi Ma   71
ECOLE PASTORALE LUTHERIENNE (IVORY). Fiana-
rantsoa, Malagasy Republic (Lutheran: American,
Malagasy, Norwegian) 1871.   72
IMERIMANDROSO COLLEGE. Imerimandroso, MLA,
Malagasy Republic (Church of Christ in Madagascar--
F.K.M.) 1922.
Library: 1922, 0, OB, OS, 3,000-1,050, F Mala-

gasy, own, F-S, SC, 6-0, Ar   73
GRAND SEMINAIRE--INSTITUT SUPERIEUR DE
  THEOLOGIE. Ambatoroka, Tananarive, Mala-
  gasy Republic (Conference Episcopale de Madagas-
  car and Congregation de la Propagande--Rome)
  1929.
  Library: 1929, 2, OB, OS, 25,000-20,000, F L,
  F-S, 89-75   74
KOLEJY TEOLOJIKA AMBOHIPOTSY. 16, rue We-
  bert, Tananarive, Malagasy Republic (Congrega-
  tional) 1869.   75
SEMINAIRE ST. PIERRE. Ambatoroka (Madecassense
  Institutium Theologie) Tananarive, Malagasy Republic (Roman Catholic).   76

Malawi
ST. ANDREW'S THEOLOGICAL COLLEGE. Likoma Is-
  land, Malawi (Anglican).   77
C.C.A.P. THEOLOGICAL COLLEGE. P.O. Nkhoma,
  Malawi (Presbyterian Church of Central Africa) 1924.
  Library: 1924, 0, OB, OS, 3,000-2,000, E, DDC,
  F-S, SC, 8-0, Ma   78

Mauritius
ST. PAUL'S THEOLOGICAL COLLEGE. Holy Trinity
  Rectory, Rose-Hill, Mauritius (Anglican Diocese of
  Mauritius), 1867.
  Library: 1867, 1, OS, 4,000-3,000, E F, 5-0   79

Mozambique
ESCOLE DOS EVANGELISTOS DE INHAMACHAFO.
  Inharrime, Mozambique (Methodist) 1922.   80
S. AGOSTINIO DE MACIENO. C. P. 63, Joao Belo,
  Mozambique (Anglican) 1902.   81
SEMINAIRE UNIDO DE RICATLA. C. P. 21, Lourenco
  Marques, Mozambique (Congregational, Methodist,
  Reformed) 1958.   82
SEMINARIO MAIOR DE CRISTO REI. Lourenco Mar-
  ques, Mozambique (Roman Catholic).   83
SEMINARIO TEOLOGICO BAPTISTA DE MOCAMBIQUE.
  Rua Herois de Marracuena, 141, Caixa Postal, 599,
  Lourenco Marques, Mozambique, P. E. (Union Bap-
  tist of Mozambique) 1960.
  Library: 1960, 1, OB, OS, 2,000-2,000, P, Classic,
  F-S, SC, 12-0, Sl Pi Ma Mu   84
TAVANE NAZARENE BIBLE TRAINING SCHOOL. Man-
  jacoz, Mozambique (Church of the Nazarene) 1954.   85

Mozambique (cont.)
COMBINE BIBLE SCHOOL AND FAMILY TRAINING.
C. P. 7, Morrumbere, Mozambique (Southeast
Africa Mission of the Methodist Episcopal Church)
1924.
Library: 1940, 1, OS, 2,500-1,200, E P, Shelves,
10-0, Ar Fi Sl Pi Ma Mu   86

Nigeria
QUA IBOE CHURCH BIBLE COLLEGE.   Ilsot, Ekang
P.O. Box 34, Abak, Eastern Nigeria, Nigeria (Qua
Iboe Church and Mission) 1941.   87
MAJOR CATHOLIC SEMINARY.   Benin City, Midwest-
ern Nigeria, Nigeria (Roman Catholic).   88
THEOLOGICAL COLLEGE OF NORTHERN NIGERIA.
P.O. Box 64, Bukuru, Northern Nigeria, Nigeria
(The Fellowship of Churches of Christ in the Sudan,
The Church of the Brethren Mission, The Sudan
United Mission) 1957.
Library: 1957, 1, OB, OS, 12,000-4,250, E, LC,
F-S, 7-3, VF   89
CATHOLIC MAJOR SEMINARY.   P.O. Box 917, Ibadan,
Western Nigeria, Nigeria (Roman Catholic).   90
IMMANUEL COLLEGE.   P.O. Box 515, Ibadan, West-
ern Nigeria, Nigeria (African Methodist) 1958.   91
UNIVERSITY OF IBADAN--DEPARTMENT OF RELI-
GIOUS STUDIES.   Ibadan, Western Nigeria, Nigeria
(Non-denominational) 1948.
Library: 1948, 1, OB, OS, 2,000-1,160, E, subject,
F-S, 3-0   92
UNIVERSITY OF IFE--DEPARTMENT OF RELIGIOUS
STUDIES.   Ibadan, Western Nigeria, Nigeria (Govern-
ment) 1961.   93
UNITED MISSIONARY SOCIETY THEOLOGICAL COLLEGE.
P.O. Box 171, Ilorin, Northern Nigeria, Nigeria
(United Missionary Society, 1819 South Main Street,
Elkhart, Indiana) 1956.
Library: 1956, 0, OS, 5,000-1,900, E, F-S, Fi Sl   94
BAPTIST PASTORS' SCHOOL, KADUNA.   Box 48, Ka-
duna, Northern Nigeria, Nigeria (Foreign Mission
Board, Southern Baptist Convention) 1949.
Library: 1949, 1, OB, OS, 10,000-4,000, E Hussa,
DDC, F-S, Pi Ma   95
EVANGELICAL LUTHERAN SEMINARY OF NIGERIA.
Obot Idim via Uyo, Nigeria (Lutheran Church--Mis-
souri Synod, Lutheran Church of Nigeria) 1949.   96
NIGERIAN BAPTIST THEOLOGICAL SEMINARY. P.O.

Box 98, Ogbomosho, Western Nigeria, Nigeria
(F. M. B. of the Southern Baptist Convention, Ni-
gerian Baptist Convention) 1898.
Library: 1898, 1, OB, 30,000-14,879, DDC, SC,
136-136, Mi Mu VF   97
MAJOR SEMINARY. P.O. All Hallows, Onitsha,
Eastern Nigeria, Nigeria (Roman Catholic).   98
TRINITY COLLEGE, UMUAHIA. P.O. Box 97, Uma-
hia, Eastern Nigeria, Nigeria (Churches of the Prov-
ince of West Africa, Methodist Church Nigerian,
Presbyterian Church of Nigeria) 1948.
Library: 1948, 1, OB, OS, 4,000-4,000, E, own,
F-S, SC, 18-15, Sl Pi Ma VF   99
UNITED CHURCHES BIBLE COLLEGE. Box 109, Uyo,
Eastern Nigeria, Nigeria (Five independent churches)
1964.   100

Nyassaland
MAJOR SEMINARY KACHEBERE. P.O. Box 185, Ft.
Manning P.O., Manning, Nyassaland (Roman Catho-
lic).   101

Portuguese East Africa
ST. AUGUSTINE'S THEOLOGICAL COLLEGE. Maciene,
C. P. 63, Vila de Joao Belo, Portuguese East Africa
(Anglican).   102

Rhodesia
SOLUSI COLLEGE. Private Bag T 189, Bulawayo,
Rhodesia (Trans-Africa Division of the Seventh-Day
Adventist Church) 1958.
Library: 1894, 2, OB, OS, 10,000-4,500, E, DDC,
20-5, Fi Sl Pi Ma VF   103

HOWARD INSTITUTE TRAINING COLLEGE. P.O. Glen-
dale, Rhodesia (Salvation Army) 1923.
Library: 1944, 0, OB, OS, ___-600, E, own, F-S,
4-0   104
AFRICAN BAPTIST THEOLOGICAL COLLEGE. P.O.
Box 657, Gwelo, Rhodesia (Baptist) 1955.   105
MURRAY PASTOR'S COLLEGE. Morgenster Mission,
Morgenster, Rhodesia (Dutch Reformed) 1936.   106
EPWORTH THEOLOGICAL COLLEGE. P.O. Park
Meadowlands, Salisbury, Rhodesia (Methodist) 1958.   107
ST. JOHN FISHER AND THOMAS MORE SEMINARY.
P.O. Box 1139, Salisbury, Rhodesia (Roman Catho-
lic).   108

Rhodesia (cont.)
UNIVERSITY COLLEGE OF RHODESIA. P. B. 1674,
   Salisbury, Rhodesia (Government) 1955.   109

Rwanda
STANLEY-SMITH THEOLOGICAL COLLEGE. E. A. R. ,
   Gahini, D. S. Kigali, Rwanda (Anglican) 1964.
   Library: 1966, 0, 5,000-615, E F native, subject
   and language, F-S, 4-0, Sl   110

Senegal
GRAND SEMINAIRE LIEBERMANN.   Sebitokame, Senegal (Roman Catholic).   111

Sierra Leone
FOURAH BAY COLLEGE.   University of Sierra Leone,
   Freetown, Sierra Leone, 1827.
   Library: 1827, 12, OB, OS, 95,000-20,000, E, DDC,
   F-S, Sl   112
SIERRA LEONE BIBLE COLLEGE.   Box 890, Freetown,
   Sierra Leone (Missionary Church Association, Ameri-
   can Wesleyan Church, United Brethren in Christ)
   1964.
   Library: 1964, 0, OS, 1,000-1,000, E, F-S, 10-0   113

South Africa, Republic of
FEDERAL THEOLOGICAL SEMINARY OF SOUTHERN
   AFRICA.   Private Bag 308, Alice, Cape Province,
   Rep. of South Africa (Bantu Congregational Church
   of South Africa, Bantu Presbyterian Church of South
   Africa, Church of the Province of South Africa--
   Anglican, Congregational Union of South Africa, Lon-
   don Missionary Society, Methodist Church of South
   Africa, Presbyterian Church of Africa, Presbyterian
   Church of South Africa, Tsonga Presbyterian Church)
   1963.
   Library: 1963, 1, OB, OS, 40,000-18,000, E, own,
   F-S, SC, 60-0, VF   114
ST. PETER'S COLLEGE.   Alice, Cape Province, Rep.
   of South Africa (Capetown Episcopal Church).   115
THEOLOGICAL SCHOOL FOR THE DUTCH REFORMED
   MISSION CHURCH. P.O. Box 182, Belleville, Cape
   Province, Rep. of South Africa (Dutch Reformed)
   1947.   116
BLOEMFONTEIN CATHEDRAL CHAPTER HOUSE.
   Bloemfontein, Cape Province, Rep. of South Africa
   (Episcopal).   117

EPISCOPAL CHURCH HOUSE.   Queen Victoria Street,
   Capetown, Cape Province, Rep. of South Africa
   (Episcopal).   118
BAPTIST BIBLE INSTITUTE.   Fort White, Debe Nek,
   Cape Province, Rep. of South Africa (Baptist) 1960.   119
DURBAN EPISCOPAL CATHEDRAL THEOLOGICAL
   LIBRARY.   Durban, Natal, Rep. of South Africa
   (Episcopal).   120
BETHEL COLLEGE.   P.O. Esdabrook via Butter-
   worth, Transkei, Rep. of South Africa.   121
JOHANNESBURG BIBLE INSTITUTE.   c/o Africa Evan-
   gelical Fellowship (S.A.G.M.) Box 91, Florida,
   Transvaal, Rep. of South Africa (Johannesburg Bible
   Institute) 1954.
   Library: 1954, 0, OB, OS, 4,000-4,000, E, DDC,
   F-S, 4-1, Sl   122
RHODES UNIVERSITY--DIVINITY SCHOOL.   P.O. Box
   94, Grahamstown, Cape Province, Rep. of South
   Africa (Methodist) 1904.   123
ST. PAUL'S COLLEGE.   Grahamstown, Cape Province,
   Rep. of South Africa (South Africa Cape Province
   Episcopal Church).   124
ST. PETER'S SEMINARY.   P.O. Box 10, Hammans-
   kraal, Rep. of South Africa (Roman Catholic) 1926.
   Library: 1926, 0, OB, OS, 10,000-6,000, E, UDC,
   20-20   125
FRED CLARK MEMORIAL AFRICAN OFFICERS TRAIN-
   ING COLLEGE.   P.O. Box 8, Pimville, Johannes-
   burg, Transvaal, Rep. of South Africa (Salvation
   Army) 1937.   126
LUTHERAN THEOLOGICAL COLLEGE.   P.O. Mapu-
   mulo, Natal, Rep. of South Africa (Governing Board
   of Lutheran Theological College) 1912.
   Library: 1912, 1, OB, OS, 10,000-6,000, E, DDC,
   F-S, 45-0   127
POTCHEFSTROOM UNIVERSITY FOR C. H. E. Pot-
   chefstroom, Transvaal, Rep. of South Africa (Re-
   formed Church of South Africa) 1869.
   Ferdinand Postma Library--Theological Branch:
   1869, 1, OB, OS, 20,000-15,000, D E
   Afrikaans, DDC, SC, 155-0, Ar   128
STOFBERG TEOLOGIESE SKOOL DINGAANSTAT.
   Dingaanstat P. B. 829, Melmoth, Natal, Rep. of
   South Africa (Dutch Reformed) 1949.   129
TEOLOGIESE SKOOL STOFBERG.   P. K. Sovenga,
   Pietersburg, Transvaal, Rep. of South Africa (Dutch
   Reformed) 1908.   130

South Africa, Republic of (cont.)
LUTHERAN THEOLOGICAL SEMINARY.   Enhlanhleni,
  P. O. Pomeroy via Dundee, Natal, Rep. of South
  Africa, 1955.   131
THEOLOGICAL SEMINARY.   64 Willow Road, Fair-
  view, Port Elizabeth, Cape Province, Rep. of South
  Africa (Moravian) 1952.   132
SAINT JOHN VIANNEY SEMINARY.   191 Main Street,
  Waterkloof, Pretoria, Transvaal, Rep. of South
  Africa (Roman Catholic Hierarchy of South Africa)
  1950.
  Library: 1950, 0, OB, OS, 50,000-25,000, E, DDC,
  100-100, Ar Fi Sl   133
UNIVERSITY OF PRETORIA--FACULTY OF THEOLOGY.
  Hillcrest, Pretoria, Transvaal, Rep. of South Africa
  (Dutch Reformed Church of Africa) 1917.   134
UNIVERSITY OF SOUTH AFRICA.   P. O. Box 392, Pre-
  toria, Transvaal, Rep. of South Africa (Interdenomi-
  national) 1946.
  Library: 1946, 1, OB, OS, ___-6,000, DDC, F-S,
  130-20   135
MARANG LUTHERAN THEOLOGICAL SEMINARY. P. O.
  Box 43, Rustenberg, Transvaal, Rep. of South Africa
  (Lutheran, Evangelical Lutheran Free Churches)
  1876.   136
THEOLOGICAL SEMINARY OF THE DUTCH REFORMED
  CHURCH.   Noordusal, Stellenbosch, Cape Province,
  Republic of South Africa (Dutch Reformed Church--Re-
  public of South Africa and South West Africa) 1859.
  Library: 1859, 2, OB, OS, 45,000-24,500, D E G,
  own and DDC, 121-69, Ar Fi Sl Mi Pi Ma Mu VF   137
UNION BIBLE INSTITUTE.   P. O. Sweetwaters, Natal,
  Rep. of South Africa (Interdenominational) 1942.   138
DECOLIGNY THEOLOGICAL SCHOOL.   Stofberg, Box
  213, Umtata, Transkei, Rep. of South Africa (Re-
  formed) 1946.   139
NEDERDUITSE GEREFORMEERDE TEOLOGIESE SKOOL
  STOFBERG.   Witsieshoek, Orange Free State, Rep.
  of South Africa (Dutch Reformed) 1960.   140
BISHOP GRAY THEOLOGICAL COLLEGE.   Zonnebloem,
  Cape Province, Rep. of South Africa (Anglican).   141

South West Africa
ST. MARY'S THEOLOGICAL SCHOOL.   Ovamboland,
  Odibo, P. O. Oshikango, South West Africa (Church
  of the Province of South Africa) 1963.
  Library: 1963, 0, OS, 2,000-1,000, E, 1-0   142

UNITED LUTHERAN THEOLOGICAL SEMINARY.
Otjimbingue via Karibil, South West Africa (Evangel-
ical Lutheran Uuambokawango Church, Evangelical
Lutheran Church of South West Africa) 1963.
Library: 1963, 3, OB, 10,000-6,000, E G Finnish
Afrikaaners, own, F-S, SC, 8-0, Ar Sl Mu   143

Sudan
BISHOP GWYNEE COLLEGE. Mundri via Juba, Sudan
(Church of Christ of Upper Nile, Anglican, Presby-
terian, Reformed Church in America, Coptic Evan-   ,
gelical).   144
ST. PAUL SEMINARY. Yei, P. I. , Tore River (Ed.
Province) Sudan (Roman Catholic).   145

Tanzania
BAPTIST THEOLOGICAL SEMINARY OF EAST AFRICA.
P.O. Box 739, Arusha, Tanzania (Foreign Mission
Board, Southern Baptist Convention) 1962.
Library: 1962, 1, OB, 15,000-3,000, DDC, F-S, 12-0   146
MAJOR SEMINARY. R. C. M. Tosamogango, P.O.
Iringa, Iringa, Tanzania (Roman Catholic).   147
ST. PHILIP'S THEOLOGICAL COLLEGE. P.O. Box
26, Kongwa, Tanzania (Church of the Province of
East Africa; Dioceses of Central Tanganyika, Victoria,
Nyanza, Morogoro, Western Tanganyika; Moravian
Church in Western Tanganyika; Moravian Church in
Southern Tanganyika) 1945.
Library: 1950, 1, OB, OS, 12,000-4,150, E Swahili,
DDC, F-S, 12-9, Pi Ma   148
ST. CYPRIAN'S COLLEGE. Ngala, P.O. Box 212,
Lindi, Tanzania (Anglican) 1932.
Library: 1932, 1, OS, 5,000-2,600, E, own, F-S,
12-0, Sl Ma   149
MAJOR SEMINARY. P.O. Box 40, Morogoro, Tan-
zania (Roman Catholic).   150
MAJOR SEMINARY OF KILIMANJARO. Kibosho, P.O.
Box 107, Moshi, Tanzania (Roman Catholic).   151
MENNONITE THEOLOGICAL COLLEGE. Box 7, Mu-
soma, Tanzania (Eastern Mennonite Board of Mis-
sions, Salunga, Pennsylvania, U.S.A.; Tanganyika
Mennonite Church) 1962.
Library: 1962, 0, OB, OS, 3,000-2,000, E Swahili,
F-S, 16-0, Sl Pi Ma   152
ST. AUGUSTINE SENIOR SEMINARY. C. M. Peramino
O. P. , Peramino, Tanzania (Roman Catholic).   153
ST. PAUL'S SEMINARY. Kipalapala P. O. , Tabora,
Tanzania (Roman Catholic).   154

LUTHERAN THEOLOGICAL COLLEGE.   Makumira,
   P.O. Box 55, Usa River, Tanzania (Lutheran
   Church in Tanzania) 1947.   155

Tunisia
GRAND SEMINAIRE.   Mutuellville, Tunisia (Roman
   Catholic).   156
FACULTE EZ-ZITOUNA DE THEOLOGIE ET DE SCI-
   ENCES RELIGIEUSES.   Rue Djama, Tunis, Tunisia,
   1960.   157

Uganda
MAJOR SEMINARY OF GABA.   Box 80, Gulu, Uganda
   (Roman Catholic).   158
CANON BARHAM DIVINITY SCHOOL.   Kabale, Uganda
   (Anglican).   159
BUGEMA MISSIONARY COLLEGE.   P.O. Namulonge,
   Kampala, Uganda (Seventh Day Adventist) 1948.   160
MAJOR SEMINARY.   P.O. Box 1871, Kampala, Uganda
   (Roman Catholic).   161
MAKERERE UNIVERSITY COLLEGE.   P.O. Box 262,
   Kampala, Uganda (Government of Uganda and Theo-
   logical Education Fund) 1922.
   Library: 1922, 7, OB, OS, 200,000-97,000, E, DDC,
   F-S, SC, 1,600-0, Ar Mi Ma   162
KATIGONDO-SEMINARY.   P.O. Box 232, Masaka,
   Uganda (Roman Catholic) 1911.
   Library: 1911, 1, OB, OS, 20,000-10,000, E F,
   DDC, F-S, 70-30   163
BULWALASI COLLEGE--BISHOP USHER-WILSON COL-
   LEGE.   P.O. Box 990, Mbale, Uganda (Anglican)
   1932.   164
BISHOP TUCKER COLLEGE.   P. O. Box 4, Mukono,
   Uganda (Anglican) 1913.   165

United Arab Republic
LIBRARY OF THE GREEK ORTHODOX PATRIARCHATE
   OF ALEXANDRIA AND ALL AFRICA.   166 Rue Port
   Said, Alexandria, United Arab Republic (Greek Ortho-
   dox Patriarchate) 952.
   Library: 952, 2, OB, 30,246-30,246, Greek, own,
   SC, 200-0   166
WESLEYAN THEOLOGICAL COLLEGE.   3 Sharia Taftish
   El Misaho, Asyut, United Arab Republic (Holiness
   Church, Methodist Church of Free Egypt) 1950.   167
COPTIC EVANGELICAL THEOLOGICAL SEMINARY.
   8 Al-Sikha Al-Bardo, Abbasiya, Cairo, United Arab

Republic (Coptic Evangelical Church) 1863.   168
GRAND SEMINAIRE CATHOLIQUE DE MEADI "ST.
    LEON-LE-GRAND." Cairo, United Arab Republic
    (Roman Catholic).   169
INSTITUTE OF COPTIC STUDIES. Anba Rueiss Build-
    ing, Ramses Avenue, Abbasiya, Cairo, United Arab
    Republic (Coptic Orthodox Church) 1953.
    Library: 1953, 1, OB, OS, 10,000-9,000, Arabic
    Coptic E F, own, F-S, SC, 15-5, Mi Pi Mu VF   170

Upper Volta
GRAND SEMINAIRE DE KOUMI. Koumi par Bobo-
    Diombosso, Upper Volta (Anglican--Conference Epis-
    copale de Haute-Volta et du Mali) 1935.
    Library: 1935, 1, OB, OS, 25,000-11,000, F, UDC,
    F-S, 97-87   171

Zambia, Republic of
MADZIMAYO THEOLOGICAL SCHOOL. Fort Jameson,
    Rep. of Zambia (Reformed Church of South Africa)
    1951.   172
UNITED CHURCH MINISTERIAL TRAINING COLLEGE.
    P.O. Box 429, Kitwe, Rep. of Zambia (United
    Church of Zambia) 1949.
    Library: 1960, 0, OS, 3,000-2,000, E, DDC, 6-0   173
ST. JOHN'S SEMINARY. P.O. Box 1521, Lusaka,
    Rep. of Zambia (Anglican Province of Central Africa)
    1947.
    Library: 1947, 0, OS, 8,000-4,400, E, own, F-S,
    2-___   174

Asia

Burma
KO THA BYN BIBLE TRAINING SCHOOL. Bassein,
Burma (Korean Baptist) 1942.   175
ZOMI BAPTIST THEOLOGICAL SCHOOL.   Falam,
Northern Chin Hills, Burma (Zomi Baptist Conven-
tion) 1953.
Library: 1953, ___-1,700, E, 7-0, Fi Pi Ma Mu   176
BURMA DIVINITY SCHOOL.   Seminary Hill, Insein,
Burma (American Baptist) 1927.   177
THEOLOGICAL TRAINING INSTITUTION--METHODIST
CHURCH.   P.O. Box 82, Mandalay, Burma (Method-
ist Church of England, Methodist Church of Upper
Burma) 1938.   178
EMMANUEL DIVINITY SCHOOL.   Mohnyin, Myitkyana
District, Upper Burma, Burma (Anglican) 1961.   179
HOLY CROSS COLLEGE.   104 Inya Road, Univ. P.O.,
Rangoon, Burma (Anglican) 1932.   180
PWO KAREN BIBLE TRAINING SCHOOL.   121 Mission
Road, Ahlone P. O. , Rangoon, Burma (Korean Bap-
tist) 1936.   181
ST. JOSEPH'S REGIONAL SEMINARY.   14, Du Bern
Road, Kamaryut P. O. , Rangoon, Burma (Roman
Catholic).   182

Ceylon
AQUINAS UNIVERSITY COLLEGE.   Colombo 8, Ceylon
(Roman Catholic) 1954.
Peter Pillai Library for Religion and Society:
1965, 2, OB, OS, 10,000-5,000, E, DDC
and Walsh, SC, 38-___   183
CEYLON TERRITORY TRAINING COLLEGE.   c/o The
Salvation Army, 77, Campbell Place, Colombo 10,
Ceylon (Salvation Army).   184
DIVINITY SCHOOL.   370 Buller's Road, Colombo, Cey-
lon (Anglican) 1851.   185
MAJOR SEMINARY.   Ampitiya, Kandy, Ceylon (Roman
Catholic).   186
DUTCH REFORMED CHURCH SEMINARY.   2 Mudaliyar

48

Avenue, Kohuwela, Nugegoda, Ceylon (Dutch Reformed Church of Ceylon--General Consistory)
1963.   187
THEOLOGICAL COLLEGE OF LANKA. Pilimatalawa,
Ceylon (Anglican, Baptist, Methodist) 1963.   188

Hong Kong
ALLIANCE BIBLE SEMINARY. 22 Peak Road, Cheung
Chau, Hong Kong (Christian and Missionary Alliance)
1899.
Library: 1950, 1, OB, 5,000-4,818, Chinese E,
DDC, F-S, 13-7, Fi Sl Pi Ma Mu   189
ASIA BAPTIST GRADUATE THEOLOGICAL SEMINARY.
Administrative Office, No. 1 Hoh Min Tin Hill Road,
Kowloon, Hong Kong (Baptist, F.M.B. of Southern
Baptist Convention and Oriental Baptist) 1960.   190
CHUNG CHI COLLEGE. Shatin, New Territories,
Hong Kong (United Board for Christian Higher Edu-
cation in Asia) 1951.
Library: 1951, 4, OB, OS, 50,000-84,645, Chinese E,
DDC and K. C. Lin, F-S, 428-198   191
CONCORDIA THEOLOGICAL SEMINARY. 68 Begonia
Road, Kowloon, Hong Kong (Lutheran Church--Mis-
souri Synod) 1954.
Library: 1954, 1, OB, OS, 5,000-5,000, Chinese
E, LC, 33-9, Ar Sl Ma Mu   192
HEAVENLY PEOPLE THEOLOGICAL SEMINARY. 412-
413 A, Wong Po Building, Hungham, Hong Kong 1963.
Mailing address: P.O. Box 5421, Hong Kong.
Library: 1963, 2, ___ -300, SC, 30-0, Sl Ma Mu   193
HOLY SPIRIT SEMINARY. Aberdeen, Hong Kong
(Roman Catholic) 1964.
Library: 1966, 0, OB, OS, 10,000-1,000, Chinese
E, DDC, F-S, 17-11, Pi Ma   194
HONG KONG BAPTIST THEOLOGICAL SEMINARY.
Homantin Hill Road, Kowloon, Hong Kong (Hong Kong
Baptist Church, Southern Baptist Mission Board)
1951.
Rankin Memorial Library: 1951, 1, OB, OS,
___ -8,154, DDC, SC, 61-30   195
HONG KONG LUTHERAN THEOLOGICAL SEMINARY.
P. O. Box 20, Shatin, New Territories, Hong Kong
(Lutheran) 1913.
Library: 1913, 2, OB, OS, 17,000-17,000, Chinese
E, DDC, 50-10, Ma   196
LOK YUK THEOLOGICAL SEMINARY. N. T. Sai Kung,
Hong Kong (Reformed--Basel Missionary Society,

Hong Kong (cont.)
  Tsung Tsi Church of Hong Kong) 1955.   197
UNION THEOLOGICAL COLLEGE.   c/o St. John's
  College, Hong Kong (Anglican).   198

India
  Andhra Pradesh
SALVATION ARMY TRAINING COLLEGE.   Nellore
  P. O. Daigamet, Andhra Pradesh, India (Salvation
  Army).   199
BAPTIST THEOLOGICAL SEMINARY.   Church Square,
  Kakinada 2, E. Godavery District, Andhra Pradesh,
  India (Baptist F. M. B.) 1908.   200
CHURCH OF GOD BIBLE SCHOOL.   Kakinada 1, An-
  dhra Pradesh, India (Church of God F. M. B.) 1961.   201
ST. JOHN'S SEMINARY.   Nellore, Andhra Pradesh,
  India (Roman Catholic).   202
ANDHRA CHRISTIAN THEOLOGICAL COLLEGE.
  Luthergiri, Rajahmundry 1, Andhra Pradesh, India
  (Anglican, Baptist Church of North and South India,
  C. S. I. , Lutheran, Methodist) 1964.   203
RAMAPATNAM BAPTIST THEOLOGICAL SEMINARY.
  Ramapatnam, Nellore District, Andhra Pradesh,
  India (American Baptist, Swedish Baptist, Telegu
  Baptist) 1874.   204

  Assam
AIJAL THEOLOGICAL SCHOOL.   Aijal, Mizo District,
  Assam, India (Presbyterian Church of Wales, Assam
  Mizo Church) 1965.   205
CHERRA THEOLOGICAL COLLEGE.   Cherrapunji,
  Assam, India (Presbyterian Church in America,
  Presbyterian Church in Wales) 1887.   206
EASTERN THEOLOGICAL COLLEGE.   Jorhat, Assam,
  India (Baptist) 1906.   207

  Bengal
BISHOP'S COLLEGE.   224 Lower Circular Road, Cal-
  cutta 17, Bengal, India (Anglican) 1820.
  Library: 1820, 0, OB, OS, 5,000-5,000, E, own,
  F-S, SC, 15-5   208
UNION THEOLOGICAL SCHOOL.   P. O. Barisha, Cal-
  cutta 8, Bengal, India (Theological Education Fund)
  1945.
  Library: 0, 1,800-1,950   209

Bihar

SANTAL THEOLOGICAL SEMINARY. P. O. Benagaria,
Parganas District, Santal, Bihar, India (Lutherans:
American, Norwegian, Danish, South Indian) 1916.   210
BISHOP HUBBACK THEOLOGICAL COLLEGE. P.O.
Murku, Ranchi District, Bihar, India (Anglican)
1870.   211
LUTHERAN THEOLOGICAL COLLEGE. Ranchi, Bihar,
India (Lutheran, Gosner Lutheran) 1872.   212
ST. ALBERT'S COLLEGE. Ranchi, Bihar, India
(Roman Catholic).   213

Goa

SEMINARIO DE RACHAL. Goa, India (Roman Catho-
lic).   214
ALL INDIA MISSION SEMINARY. Pilar, Goa, India
(Missionary Society of St. Francis Xavier, Pilar,
Goa) 1942.
Library: 1945, 4, OB, OS, 60,000-5,000, E, DDC,
F-S, SC, 93-75, Ma VF   215

Gujarat

GUJARAT UNITED SCHOOL OF THEOLOGY. Ellis
Bridge, Ahmadabad 6, India (Brethren, Methodist,
United Church of North India) 1942.   216

Kerala

ST. JOSEPH'S PONTIFICAL SEMINARY. Alwaye,
Kerala, India (Roman Catholic) 1692.
Library: 1692, 2, OB, OS, 80,000-52,000, E,
DDC, F-S, 225-180, Ar Sl Ma   217
MAR THOMA SYRIAN THEOLOGICAL SEMINARY.
Kottayam-l, Kerala, India (Mar Thoma Syrian
Church) 1926.
Library: 1926, 2, OB, 4,000-3,000, E, F-S, 12-4   218
ORTHODOX THEOLOGICAL SEMINARY. Kottayam,
Kerala, India (Orthodox Syrian) 1815.
Library: 1815, 1, OB, 15,000-7,500, E, DDC, F-S,
12-5   219
KERALA UNITED THEOLOGICAL SEMINARY. Medical
College P.O., Trivandrum 11, Kerala, India (Angli-
can, C.S.I., Congregational, Reformed) 1943.   220

Madhya Pradesh

LEONARD THEOLOGICAL COLLEGE. Jabalpur, Madhya
Pradesh, India (C.S.I., United Church of Canada,
Mar Thoma, Methodist, Presbyterian, United Church

Madhya Pradesh (cont.)
of North India) 1872.   221

Madras
GURUKUL LUTHERAN THEOLOGICAL COLLEGE AND
RESEARCH INSTITUTE. 60/61 Puraswalkam, High
Road, Kilpauk, Madras 10, India (Lutheran) 1931.   222
HINDUSTAN BIBLE INSTITUTE. 2, Madavakam Tank
Road, Kilpauk, Madras 10, India (Interdenomination-
al) 1952.
Library: 1952, 2, OB, OS, 10,000-6,000, E, DDC,
F-S, 20-0, Sl Pi Ma Mu   223
MADRAS BIBLE SEMINARY. 5, Waddell Road, Kilpauk,
Madras 10, India (Oriental Missionary Society)
1953.   224
CONCORDIA SEMINARY. Nagercoil 1, Madras, India
(India Evangelical Lutheran Church) 1924.
Library: 1924, 1, OB, OS, 11,000-7,700, E Malay-
sian Tamil, DDC, SC, 25-10, Ma   225
SACRED HEART SEMINARY. Poonamallee, Madras
56, India (Roman Catholic) 1936.
Library: 1936, 0, OB, OS, 15,000-10,000, card,
F-S, 80-55   226
ST. PAUL SEMINARY. Tiruchirapalli, Madras, India
(Roman Catholic)   227
TAMILNAD THEOLOGICAL COLLEGE. Tirumaraiyur,
Nazareth, Tirunelveli, Madras, India (Methodist).   228
THEOLOGICAL SEMINARY. Tirumaraiyur via Naza-
reth, Tirunelveli District, Madras, India (C.S.T.
T.A.) 1936.   229
TAMIL EVANGELICAL LUTHERAN CHURCH DIVINITY
SCHOOL. Tranquebar, Tanjore District, Madras,
India (Tamil Evangelical Lutheran Church) 1954.
Library: 1954, 0, OB, 4,000-3,100, E, A-Z, 11-8,
Ma   230

Maharashtra
THEOLOGICAL COLLEGE. Badra, Bombay, Maha-
rashtra, India (Roman Catholic).   231
UNION BIBLICAL SEMINARY. Yestmal, Bombay,
Maharashtra, India (Union Board of 22 Mission
Boards) 1953.   232
ST. CHARLES SEMINARY. Seminary Hill, Nagpur-1,
Maharashtra, India (Roman Catholic--Diocese of
Nagpur) 1958.
Library: 1958, 0, OB, OS, 10,000-3,000, E, DDC,
F-S, 50-40   233

PONTIFICAL ATHENAEUM POONA. Poona 14, Maharashtra, India (Roman Catholic--Society of Jesus) 1955.
Library: 1955, 1, OB, OS, 150,000-50,000, E, own, 110-110   234
UNITED THEOLOGICAL COLLEGE OF WESTERN INDIA. 1-A Prince of Wales Drive, Poona 1, Maharashtra, India (Anglican, Brethren, Congregational, Methodist, Presbyterian, United Church of North India) 1878.   235

Mysore
ST. PETER'S SEMINARY. Molleswaram, Bangalore, Mysore, India (Roman Catholic).   236
SOUTHERN ASIA BIBLE COLLEGE. 15 Cock Burn Road, Bangalore 1, Mysore, India (Assemblies of God) 1951.
Library: 1956, 1, OB, OS, 5,000-5,288, E, DDC, 13-2, Ma   237
UNITED THEOLOGICAL COLLEGE OF SOUTH INDIA AND CEYLON. 17 Miller's Road, Bangalore 6, Mysore, India (Church of South India, Mar Thoma Church, U. K. Switzerland and Denmark Foreign Mission Boards, U. S. A. Foreign Mission Boards) 1910.
Library: 1941, 3, OB, OS, 40,000-20,000, E Indian, DDC, F-S 100-90, Ar Sl Ma VF   238
SOUTH INDIA BIBLE INSTITUTE. Anadagiri, Box 20, Bangarapet, Mysore, India (World Gospel Mission) 1937.   239
KARNATAKA THEOLOGICAL COLLEGE. Balmatta, Mangalore 1, Mysore, India (C.S.I., Reformed) 1965.   240
ST. JOSEPH'S SEMINARY. B.P. 503, Mangalore 2, Mysore, India (Roman Catholic--Society of Jesus) 1878.
Library: 1878, 1, OB, OS,   -24,300, E, own, F-S, SC, 84-55, Ar Fi Sl Pi Ma VF   241

Orissa
THEOLOGICAL COLLEGE. Cuttack, Orissa, India (Baptist) 1845.   242
JENSEN THEOLOGICAL COLLEGE AND BIBLE SCHOOL. Kotopad, Karaput District, Orissa, India (Lutheran: Schleswig-Holstein, Jeypore) 1897.   243

Uttar Pradesh
ALLAHABAD BIBLE SEMINARY. 20 Stanley Road,

Uttar Pradesh (cont.)
    Allahabad, Uttar Pradesh, India (Oriental Mission-
    ary Society) 1942.   244
ST. JOSEPH'S SEMINARY. 4, Tashkent Road, Allah-
    abad, Uttar Pradesh, India (Roman Catholic) 1914.
    Library: 1920, 2, OB, 10,000-7,000, E, A-Z, F-S,
    25-20, Ma   245
NORTH INDIA THEOLOGICAL COLLEGE. 106 Civil
    Lines, Bareilly, Uttar Pradesh, India (Baptist Union
    of North India; Church of India, Pakistan, Burma
    and Ceylon; Methodist Church--British; Methodist
    Church in Southern Asia; United Church of Northern
    India) 1874, 1965.
    Library: 1965, 1, OB, ___-8,136, E Hindu Urdu,
    DDC, 40-16 Ma   246
GNAN DAN BHAWAN. Christnaga, Benares, Uttar
    Pradesh, India (Roman Catholic).   247

    West Bengal
ST. MARY'S THEOLOGICAL COLLEGE. St. Mary's
    Hill, P.O. Kurseong, Darjeeling District, West
    Bengal, India (Roman Catholic--Society of Jesus)
    1889.
    Library: 1889, 2, OB, OS, 75,000-63,000, E F G,
    British Museum Modified, F-S, 336-264   248
SERAMPORE COLLEGE. District Hooghly, West Bengal,
    India (Serampore College Council) 1818.
    Library: 1818, 2, OB, OS, 25,000-13,500, E, own,
    F-S, SC, 50-21, Ar Fi Sl Mi Pi Ma   249

Indonesia
SEKOLAH THEOLOGIA GEREDJA PROTESTAN MALU-
    KU. Tanah Lapang, Ketjil, Ambon, Moluccas, Indo-
    nesia (Moluccan Protestant Church) 1965.   250
AKADEMI THEOLOGIA G.K.E. Djalan Djenderal,
    Sudirman 6, Bandjarmasin, Indonesia (Geredja Kali-
    mantan Evangelis) 1932.
    Library: 1932, 1, OB, OS, 9,000-2,000, E G, F-S,
    14-0   251
SEMINARI AGUNG. Karmel, Batu, Diawa Timur,
    Indonesia (Roman Catholic).   252
SEMINARI AGUNG. Gariun, Blitar, Indonesia (Roman
    Catholic).   253
SEKOLAH TINGGI THEOLOGIA. Djalan Pegangsaan
    Timur 27, Djakarta III/20, Indonesia (N.C.C. of
    Indonesia--15 bodies) 1954.   254
SEKOLAH THEOLOGIA BALWIJOTO. Djl. Sukun 18,

Malang, Djawa Timur, Indonesia (Reformed, Protestant Churches of Central and Eastern Java) 1927.   255
SOUTH EAST ASIA BIBLE COLLEGE. P.O. Box 74, Malang, Djatim, Indonesia (Evangelize China Fellowship) 1952.
Library: 1952, 0, 6,000-2,000, Chinese E Indonesian, own, F-S, 6-0, Ma   256
SEKOLAH TINGGI THEOLOGIA. "Duta Watjana" Djl. Dr. Wahidin Sudirohusodo 21, Jogjakarta, Indonesia (Theological Education Fund and Fund for Theological Education) 1962.
Library: 1962, 2, OB, OS, 10,000-8,000, E, UTS, 35-25   257
SEMINARI AGUNG. Djalan Telemojo 2, Jojkarta, Indonesia (Roman Catholic).   258
SEKOLAH THEOLOGIA GMIT. Kotakpos, Kupang, Indonesia (Protestant Church of Timur) 1960.   259
PERGURUAN THEOLOGIA UNTUK INDONESIA TIMUR. Tjenderawasih L R 321/7B, P.O. Box 140, Makassar, Indonesia (14 churches of the eastern part of Indonesia, F.T.E., T.E.F., E.U.B., U.C.C. in the U.S.A., Herwormde Kerk and de Sireformurde Kerk in Nederland) 1947.
Library: 1947, 1, OB, OS, 50,000-4,847, DDC, F-S, 6-0   260
SEMINARI AGUNG PINELENG. Djalan Jos Sudarso 1, Manado (Sulut) Indonesia (Diocese of Manado of the Roman Catholic Church) 1955.
Library: 1955, 3, OB, OS, 10,000-7,000, D E, Decimal, F-S, 22-0, Ar   261
SEMINARI AGUNG. Ledalero, Maumere (Flores) Indonesia (Roman Catholic).   262
AKADEMIA KRISTEN "WIJATA WATJANA." Djalan Pendjowi 48, Pati, Java, Indonesia (Mennonite) 1965.   263
SEMINARI AGUNG. Parapat p/a Pastoral Katolik, Djalan Sibolga 21, Pematangsiantar, Sumatra, Indonesia (Roman Catholic).   264
UNIVERSITAS H.K.B.P. NOMMENSEN SEKOLAH THEOLOGIA. Djalan Asahan 4, Pematangsiantar, Sumatra, Indonesia (Lutheran, Methodist) 1954.   265
SEMINARI THEOLOGIA BAPTIS DE INDONESIA. Box 205, Semarang, Indonesia (Baptist--F.M.B. of the Southern Baptist Convention, Richmond, Virginia) 1954.
Library: 1954, 0, OB, OS, ___-11,000, E Indonesian, UTS, F-S, 24-5   266

Indonesia (cont.)
PERGURUAN THEOLOGIA GKI. Postbox 125, Abe-
pure, Sukarnapure, West-Irian, Indonesia (Evan-
gelical Christian Church of West-Irian--GKI) 1967.
Library: 1967, 0, OB, OS, 2,500-2,250, D E, F-
S, 1-0, Ar Sl Pi Ma VF   267
SEMINARI AGUNG. Biara Padua, Tjitjurug, Djawa
Barat, Indonesia (Roman Catholic).   268
UNIVERSITAS KRISTEN I.T.--FAKULTAS THEOLOGIA.
Kurango-Tomohon, Utara, Sulawesi, Indonesia (Mina-
hasa Christian Evangelical Church) 1962.   269

Iran
DANECHGABE'O FACULTY OF THEOLOGY. Machad,
Iran, 1938.   270

Iraq
ST. PETER'S SEMINARY "PATRIARCHAL CHALDEA."
Mossoul, Iraq (Roman Catholic).   271
SEMINAIRE ST. JEAN. Mossoul, Iraq (Roman Catho-
lic).   272

Israel
UNIVERSITA BAR-ILAN, RAMAT-GAN--FACULTY OF
JEWISH AND HEBREW STUDIES. Bar-Ilan, Israel
(Jewish) 1952.   273
ARMENIAN PATRIARCHATE. Old City, Jerusalem,
Israel (Armenian Orthodox).
Gulbenkian Library: 1929, 1, OB, 50,000-50,000,
Armenian, DDC, F-S, SC, 280-   274
CENTRAL RABBINICAL LIBRARY OF ISRAEL. Hevron
Street, Jerusalem, Israel (Jewish) 1953.   275
ECOLE BIBLIQUE ET ARCHAEOLOGIQUE FRANCAISE.
Convent des Dominicans de St. Etienne, P.O. Box
53, via Amman, Jerusalem, Israel (Roman Catholic)
1890.   276
HA' UNIVERSITA HA' IVRITH--FACULTY OF HUMANI-
TIES. Jerusalem, Israel (Jewish) 1925.   277
HARRY FISCHEL INSTITUTE. 7 Israel Aaron Fischel
Street, Bokharim Quarter, Jerusalem, Israel (Jew-
ish) 1932.
Library: 1932, 21, OB, 20,000-5,000, own   278
HEBREW UNION COLLEGE AND JEWISH INSTITUTE
OF RELIGION. 13 King David Way, Jerusalem,
Israel (Reformed Judaism).   279
PONTIFICAL BIBLICAL INSTITUTE. P.O. Box 497,
3, Paul-Emile-Botta, Jerusalem, Israel (Roman

Catholic--Society of Jesus) 1927.
Library: 1927, 2, OS, 15,000-10,000, authors,
150-150, Ma   280
ST. ANNE'S SEMINARY. P.O. Box 79/0079, Old
City, Jerusalem, Israel (Roman Catholic--White
Fathers) 1882.
Library: 1882, 2, OB, OS, 50,000-20,000, LC,
160-100   281
ST. GEORGE'S COLLEGE. Jerusalem, Israel (Angli-
can) 1845.
Library: 1892, 1, OB, OS, 20,000-14,000, Arabic,
E F G, DDC, 24-10, Ma   282
SEMINAIRE GREC CATHOLIQUE "STE. ANNE. " Via
Beyrouth-Amman, Jerusalem, Israel (Roman Catho-
lic).   283

Japan
ST. SULPICE INTERDIOCESAN SEMINARY. Igoo
Shinshoji, Katae, Fukuoka City, Japan (Roman
Catholic) 1951.
Library: 1951, 1, OB, 30,000-22,500, E F J L,
DDC, F-S, 100-__, Fi Pi   284
SEINAN GAKUIN UNIVERSITY AND BIBLE SCHOOL--
THEOLOGY DEPARTMENT. 408, Hoshiguma,
Fukuoka City, Japan (Nippon Baptist Remmei--
Japan Baptist Convention) 1924.
Library: 1924, 1, OS, 30,000-25,037, E G J,
NDC, F-S, 86-__, Fi Mi Ma Mu   285
NORTHEAST BIBLE INSTITUTE. Tsutsumi, Sukagawa
Shi, Fukushimaken, Japan (Interdenominational).   286
JAPAN ALLIANCE BIBLE COLLEGE. 255 Itsukaitchi
Machi, Saiki Gun, Hiroshima Ken, Japan (Christian
Missionary Alliance).   287
KOBE LUTHERAN THEOLOGICAL SEMINARY. 2-3
Nakajimadori, Fukiai-ku, Kobe, Japan (Norwegian
Lutheran Mission) 1957.
Library: 1957, 1, OS, 10,000-__, own, F-S, 8-0   288
KOBE REFORMED THEOLOGICAL SEMINARY. 10
Kotobuki Takaha Nada, Kobe, Japan (Reformed)
1947.   289
BISHOP WILLIAMS' SEMINARY. Korasumaru-Dori,
Shimotachiuri-Agaru, Kamikyo-ku, Kyoto, Japan
(Anglican) 1948.   290
DOSHISHA UNIVERSITY--SCHOOL OF THEOLOGY.
Nishijin, Kyoto, Japan, 1875.
Library: 1875, 4, OB, OS, 65,200-__, E, NDC,
SC, 243-2, Ar Sl Mi Pi Ma VF   291

Japan (cont.)
KWANSEIGAKUIN UNIVERSITY--DEPARTMENT OF
   THEOLOGY. 1-2 Uegahara, Nishinomiya City,
   Hyogo Prefecture, Japan, 1889.
   Library: 1889, 1, OB, 12,000-8,000, E G, NDC,
   94-0   292
OSAKA CHRISTIAN COLLEGE AND THEOLOGICAL
   SEMINARY. 81-1 Chome, Maruyama-dori, Abeno-
   ku, Osaka, Japan (Methodist) 1903.   293
OSAKA BIBLICAL SEMINARY. 1-20, 2 Chome, Soen,
   Ikeda Shi, Osaka Fu, Japan (Mennonite Brethren
   Board of Church Missions, Baptist General Confer-
   ence, North American Baptist Convention) 1957.
   Library: 1957, 2, OB, OS, 13,000-3,300, E J,
   Yale, 45-26, Sl Pi Ma   294
AOYAMAGAKUIN--THEOLOGICAL DEPARTMENT. 4-
   25, Shibuya 4, Shibuya-ku, Tokyo, Japan, 1874.
   Library: 1929, 1, OB, OS, 6,000-___, E G, D.C.,
   28-0, Ma   295
CENTRAL BIBLE INSTITUTE. 430-1 San Chome,
   Komagome Toshima Ku, Tokyo, Japan (Assemblies
   of God).   296
CENTRAL THEOLOGICAL COLLEGE. 8, 2-Chome
   Tamagawa Makaumachi, Setagaya ku, Tokyo, Japan
   (Anglican) 1911.   297
JAPAN BIBLE SEMINARY. 665-2 Narimune, Suginami
   ku, Tokyo, Japan (Disciples, Interdenominational)
   1958.   298
JAPAN BIBLICAL SEMINARY. 492, 1-Chome, Shimo-
   Ochiai, Shinjuku-ku, Tokyo, Japan, 1946.
   Library: 1946, 3, OB, 20,000-6,500, UTS, F-S,
   55-6, Ma Mu   299
JAPAN CHRISTIAN THEOLOGICAL SEMINARY. 273-1
   chome, Horinouchi, Suginami-ku, Tokyo, Japan (Inde-
   pendent) 1966.
   Library: 1949, 1, OS, 4,000-4,000, E J, DDC, F-S,
   -2   300
JAPAN LUTHERAN THEOLOGICAL COLLEGE AND
   SEMINARY. 13-38, 2-Chome, Shirasagi, Nakano-ku,
   Tokyo, Japan (Japan Evangelical Lutheran Church)
   1909.
   Library: 1909, 2, OB, OS, 27,000-25,000, E G L,
   DDC, SC, 68-0   301
JOCHI DAIGAKU--FACULTY OF THEOLOGY. 7 Kiochio,
   Chijoda-ku, Tokyo, Japan (Roman Catholic--Society
   of Jesus) 1913.   302
MAJOR SEMINARY--THEOLOGICAL SECTION. 2 Chome,

Sekimachi, Shakujii, Nerima-ku, Tokyo, Japan
(Roman Catholic). 303
RIKKYO (ST. PAUL'S) UNIVERSITY--THE COLLEGE
OF THE ARTS, DEPARTMENT OF CHRISTIAN
STUDIES. Ikebukuro, Tokyo, Japan (Anglican) 1949. 304
SALVATION ARMY TRAINING COLLEGE FOR OFFI-
CERS. 5-39 Wada 1 Chome, Suginami-ku, Tokyo,
Japan (Salvation Army) 1907. 305
THEOLOGICAL TRAINING PROGRAM. 16 1-Chome,
Fijimi-cho, Chiyoda-ku, Tokyo, Japan (Lutheran
Church--Missouri Synod) 1953. 306
TOKYO CHRISTIAN COLLEGE. 8453 Yaho, Kunitachi-
shi, Tokyo, Japan (Evangelical Alliance Mission)
1955.
Library: 1955, 2, OS, 15,000-15,000, NDC, 73-
73 307
TOKYO ORTHODOX THEOLOGICAL SEMINARY. 1-4
Surugadai Kanda, Chiyoda-ku, Tokyo, Japan (Japa-
nese Orthodox) 1954. 308
TOKYO UNION THEOLOGICAL SEMINARY. 264 Igu-
chi, Mitaka-shi, Tokyo, Japan (Church of Christ of
Japan--KyoDan) 1963.
Library: 1963, 3, OB, OS, 60,000-50,000, E F G
J, UTS, F-S, SC, 60-60, Fi Sl Ma Mu 309
TSURUKAWA RURAL INSTITUTE. 2024 Nozuta,
Machida-shi, Tokyo, Japan (Tsurukawa Rural Insti-
tute of the United Church of Christ in Japan) 1948.
Library: 1948, 2, OB, OS, 7,000-4,816, E J, DDC,
F-S, SC, 38-25, Ma VF 310
KANTO GAUKIN UNIVERSITY--COLLEGE OF THEOLOGY.
Mutsuura, Kanazawa Ku, Yokohama, Japan (Baptist)
1884. 311

Jordan
SEMINARY OF THE LATIN PATRIARCHATE OF
JERUSALEM. Beit Jala, Jordan (Latin Patriarchate
of Jerusalem) 1852.
Latin Patriarchal Library: 1852, 2, OB, OS,
10,000-7,000, Arabic E F, Decimal, F-S, 23-___,
Ar Pi Sl Mu 312

Korea
HO NAM THEOLOGICAL SEMINARY. 511 Paek Un
Dong, Kwangju, Chulla Namdo, Korea (Presby-
terian) 1961. 313
YONG-MOON-SAN PRAYER HOUSE, MONASTERY AND
NUNNERY. 274 Nuengchi-dong, Umo-Myon, Kum-

<u>Korea</u> (cont.)
   nung-gun, Kyongsangbuk-do, Korea (Independent)
   1957.
   Yong-Moon-San Gideons Library: 1957, 10, OB,
   OS, 300,000-30,000, J Korean, A-Z, F-S, 20-10,
   Sl Pi Ma Mu VF   314
KORYU THEOLOGICAL SEMINARY. P.O. Box 190,
   Pusan, Korea (Korean Presbyterian Church--Koryu
   Group) 1946.
   Library: 1947, 1, OB, OS, 20,000-10,000, E, own,
   35-4   315
PUSAN UNION SEMINARY.   No. 60 San Geo-Je-Dong,
   Dong-Nea-Ku, Pusan, Korea (Presbyterian) 1962.   316
BIBLICAL COLLEGE.   181 Chungyang-ri, Tongdaemun-
   ku, Seoul, Korea (Independent) 1962.   317
CALVIN THEOLOGICAL SEMINARY.   58-19 Susomoon-
   Dong, West Gate, Seoul, Korea (Calvin Seminary
   Board of Trustees) 1954.   318
CENTRAL THEOLOGICAL SEMINARY.   17 Dongzadong,
   Chungku, Seoul, Korea (Independent) 1947.   319
HAN YANG THEOLOGICAL SEMINARY.   Mt 6-1, Don-am
   Dong, Sungbuk-ku, Seoul, Korea, 1956.
   Library: 1960, 1, 2,000-80, 5-0, Ma   320
HAN-KUK THEOLOGICAL SEMINARY.   120 Suyu-Dong,
   Sungbuk-ku, Seoul, Korea (United Church of Canada)
   1940.   321
KOREA CHRISTIAN COLLEGE--THEOLOGY INSTITUTE.
   5-198 Hyochang-dong, Yongsanku, Seoul, Korea
   (Christian Churches in Korea, Christian Churches in
   U.S. and Australia, Churches of Christ in U.S. and
   Australia) 1965.
   Library: 1965, 1, OB, 15,000-4,000, Korean, KDC,
   12-2, Fi Sl Ma Mu VF   322
KOREAN PRESBYTERIAN GENERAL ASSEMBLY THEO-
   LOGICAL SEMINARY.   P.O. Box 20, Yong-San-Ku,
   Seoul, Korea (Korean Presbyterian Church) 1901.
   Library: 1901, 1, OB, OS, 15,000-___, E, West-
   minster Philadelphia, 70-3, Ma   323
KOREAN UNION COLLEGE.   Box 1243, Seoul, Korea
   (Seventh-Day Adventist Mission) 1906.
   Library: 1961, 2, OB, 20,000-___, DDC, 43-15,
   Ar Sl Pi Ma Mu VF   324
METHODIST THEOLOGICAL SEMINARY.   P.O. Box 45
   West Gate, Seoul, Korea (Methodist--U.S.A.) 1905.   325
PRESBYTERIAN THEOLOGICAL SEMINARY.   353
   Kwangjang-dong, Sungdong-ku, Seoul, Korea (Presby-
   terian Church in Korea) 1901.

Library: 1960, 1, OB, 50,000-___, DDC, F-S,
50-10   326
ST. MICHAEL'S THEOLOGICAL COLLEGE. P.O.
Box 7, Orgu Dong, Seoul, Korea, 1957.
Library: 1957, 1, OB, 16,000-___, E, DDC, F-S,
SC, 15-0, Ar Mu   327
SALVATION ARMY OFFICERS TRAINING COLLEGE.
International P.O. Box 1192, Seoul, Korea (Salva-
tion Army).   328
SEOUL BIBLE SEMINARY. Yuk Chung Dong 42-1, Sae
Dae Moon Ku, Seoul, Korea (Christian Churches of
Christ in America) 1945.   329
SEOUL PRESBYTERIAN THEOLOGICAL SEMINARY.
132-7 1-ka, Do-Dong, Chung-ku, Seoul, Korea
(Presbyterian) 1954.   330
SEOUL THEOLOGICAL COLLEGE. 3 Ka, Choong
Chong Ro, Suhdai moor Ku, Seoul, Korea (Korea
Holiness Church) 1909.
Library: 1909, 2, OB, 15,000-10,000, E Korean,
F-S, SC, 22-0   331
YONSEI UNIVERSITY--UNITED GRADUATE SCHOOL
OF THEOLOGY.   134 Shin Chon Dong, West Gate
Ku, Seoul, Korea (Theological Education Fund)
1964.
Library: 1964, 1, OS, 4,000-2,797, DDC, F-S,
65-0   332
HAN-NAM THEOLOGICAL SEMINARY. 1223 Bongduk-
Dong, Taegu, Korea (Presbyterian) 1953.   333
TAEGU PRESBYTERIAN THEOLOGICAL SEMINARY.
5 Nam-San Dong, Taegu, Korea (Presbyterian) 1950. 334
KOREA BAPTIST THEOLOGICAL SEMINARY. Mok
Dong, San 7, Taejon, Korea (Southern Baptist Con-
vention F.M.B.) 1954.
Library: 1955, 2, OB, OS, 20,000-4,000, DDC, F-
S, SC, 35-0, Sl Pi   335
TAEJON METHODIST SEMINARY. 24 Mokdong, Taejon,
Korea (Methodist) 1954.   336
TAEJON PRESBYTERIAN THEOLOGICAL SEMINARY.
Ojungdong, Taejon, Korea (Presbyterian) 1955.   337

Lebanon
ARMENIAN THEOLOGICAL SEMINARY. Armenian
Catholicosate of Cilicia, Antelias, Lebanon (Catholic-
osate of Cilicia--Armenian Orthodox Church) 1931.
Library: 1931, 1, OB, OS, 30,000-20,000, Armeni-
an, Author and Title, SC, 85-___, Ar Sl Mi Pi Ma
Mu   338

AMERICAN UNIVERSITY OF BEIRUT.   Beirut, Lebanon,
1866.
  Library: 1866, 1, OB, OS, ___-6,500, Arabic E,
  DDC, 180-150, Ar Mi Ma VF⎺⎺⎺   339
ARAB BAPTIST THEOLOGICAL SEMINARY.   P.O.
  Box 5232, Beirut, Lebanon (Near East Baptist Mis-
  sion, Southern Baptist Convention F.M.B.) 1960.
  Library: 1960, 1, OB, OS, 6,000-3,471, E, DDC,
  12-__, Ma VF   340
LEBANON BIBLE INSTITUTE.   Box 166, Beirut, Leba-
  non (Lebanon Evangelical Mission) 1937.   341
NAZARENE BIBLE SCHOOL.   Box 2328, Ashrefieh-
  Sioufi, Beirut, Lebanon (Church of the Nazarene)
  1954.
  Library: 1954, 1, OB, OS, 10,000-3,500, Arabic
  E, DDC, Sl Pi Ma Mu   342
NEAR EAST SCHOOL OF THEOLOGY.   Box 235, Bei-
  rut, Lebanon (Union of Armenian Evangelical Churches
  in the Near East; Arab Evangelical Synod of Lebanon
  and Syria; Arab Episcopal Community of Syria, Leba-
  non and Jordan; United Church Board of World Minis-
  tries; Commission on Ecumenical Mission and Rela-
  tions of the United Presbyterian Church, U.S.A.) 1875.
  Library: 1875, 1, OB, OS, 30,000-26,000, E, UTS,
  127-40, Ar Mi Ma VF   343
UNIVERSITE SAINT JOSEPH--BIBLIOTHEQUE ORI-
  ENTALE.   P.O. Box 293, Beirut, Lebanon (Roman
  Catholic) 1881.
  Bibliotheque Orientale: 1896, 8, OB, 250,000-
  145,000, Arabic F, own, SC, 600-500   344
SEMINAIRE SYRIEN CATOLIQUE.   Charfe, Harissa,
  Lebanon (Roman Catholic).   345
SEMINAIRE "ST. ANTOINE DE PADOUE." Karmsadde,
  Lebanon (Roman Catholic).   346
GRAND SEMINAIRE MARONITE.   Ksrounan, Mar Abda,
  Lebanon (Roman Catholic).   347
BELMONT THEOLOGICAL SEMINARY.   P.O. Box 100,
  Tripoli, Lebanon (Eastern Orthodox) 1879.   348
ST. APHRAIM COLLEGE.   Zahle, Lebanon (Syrian
  Orthodox Church of Antioch) 1939.   349

Macao
SEMINAR SAN JOSE.   Macao, Macao (Roman Catholic).   350

Malaysia, Federation of
HOUSE OF THE EPIPHANY THEOLOGICAL COLLEGE.

Kuching, Sarawak, Malaysia (Anglican).   351
COLLEGE GENERAL. Pulo Tiku, Penang, Malaya,
Malaysia (Roman Catholic).   352
MALAYSIA BAPTIST THEOLOGICAL SEMINARY. 35
Anson Road, Penang, Malaya, Malaysia (American
Baptist) 1953.   353
METHODIST THEOLOGICAL SCHOOL. P.O. Box 78,
Sibu, Sarawak, Malaysia (Methodist) 1953.   354

Pakistan
BIRISIRI BIBLE AND TRAINING INSTITUTE. Baptist
Mission, P.O. Birisiri, District Mymensingh, East
Pakistan, Pakistan (Baptist) 1921.   355
GUJRANWALA THEOLOGICAL SEMINARY. P.O. Box
13, Gujranwala, West Pakistan, Pakistan (Anglican,
A.R. Presbyterian, Methodist, United Church of
Pakistan, United Presbyterian) 1877.
Library: 1912, 1, OB, OS, 15,000-14,200, E Urdu,
DDC, F-S, SC, 60-10, Ar Sl Pi Ma   356
REGIONAL SEMINARY OF CHRIST THE KING. c/o St.
Patrick's Cathedral, Karachi-3, West Pakistan, Paki-
stan (The Most Reverend Hierarchy of West Pakistan)
1957.
Library: 1940, 2, OB, OS, 40,000-13,000, E, own,
180-___   357

Philippines, The
FACULTER THEOLOGIE S. ROBERTI BELLARMINO.
P.O. Box 143, Baguio City, The Philippines (Roman
Catholic) 1927.   358
LUTHERAN THEOLOGICAL SEMINARY. 8 South Drive,
P.O. Box 16, Baguio City, The Philippines (Lutheran
Church--Missouri Synod) 1955.
Library: 1955, 1, OS, 10,000-8,000, E, LC, 127-
79, Ar Sl Ma VF   359
PHILIPPINE BAPTIST THEOLOGICAL SEMINARY. P.O.
Box 7, Baguio City, Luzon, The Philippines (Baptist--
Southern Baptist Convention) 1952.
Library: 1952, 1, OB, OS, 15,000-10,000, E, DDC,
F-S, SC, 22-3, Pi Mi Ma Mu   360
ARCHDIOCESAN MAJOR SEMINARY OF SAN CARLOS.
Mabolo, Cebu City, The Philippines (Roman Catholic).361
UNION THEOLOGICAL SEMINARY, PHILIPPINES. Das-
marinas Cavite, The Philippines. Mailing address:
Box 841, Manila, P.I. (Methodist Church and United
Church of Christ in the Philippines, Presbyterian,
E.U.B., Disciples, United Church) 1907.

Philippines, The (cont.)
  Library: 1907, 2, OB, OS, 100,000-14,189, E,
  UTS, F-S, 150-___, Ma VF   362
ST. FRANCIS XAVIER SEMINARY. Catalunan Grande,
  P.O. Box 189, Davao City, The Philippines (Roman
  Catholic).   363
SILLIMAN UNIVERSITY--COLLEGE OF THEOLOGY.
  Dumaguete City, The Philippines (Congregational,
  E.U.B., Presbyterian, United Church of Christ)
  1901.
  Library: 1906   364
NORTHERN CHRISTIAN COLLEGE--COLLEGE OF THE-
  OLOGY. P.O. Box 105, Laoag, Ilocos North, Luzon,
  The Philippines (Congregationalist, United Church of
  Christ in the Philippines) 1946.   365
ARCHDIOCESAN MAJOR SEMINARY. Vigan, Ilocos Sur,
  The Philippines (Roman Catholic) 1900.
  Library: 1955, 6, OB, OS, 10,000-8,000, E, DDC,
  50-15, Ma VF   366
CENTRAL PHILIPPINE UNIVERSITY. Iloilo City, The
  Philippines (Convention of Philippine Churches and
  American Baptist Foreign Mission Society) 1905.
  Library: 1905, 1, OB, OS, ___-7,145, E, DDC,
  43-31, Pi Ma VF   367
SAINT VINCENT FERRER SEMINARY. Jaro, Iloilo
  City, The Philippines (Roman Catholic) 1869.
  Library: 1869, 2, OB, 10,000-3,000, E S, DDC,
  F-S, 14-0   368
ST. ANDREW'S THEOLOGICAL SEMINARY. P.O. Box
  3167, Manila, The Philippines (Protestant Episcopal
  Church U.S.A.) 1947.
  Bishop Mosher Memorial Library: 1947, 2, OB, OS,
  20,000-___, E, DDC, SC, 250-8, Ar Fi Sl Pi Ma
  Mu VF   369
SALVATION ARMY TRAINING INSTITUTE. 1065-C
  Ayala Street, Singalong, Manila, The Philippines
  (Salvation Army) 1938.   370
SEMINARIO CONCILIAR DE SAN CARLOS. Guadalupe,
  Makati, Rizal, Manila, The Philippines (Roman
  Catholic).   371
NO ENTRY.   372
UNIVERSITY OF SANTO TOMAS. Espana, Manila, The
  Philippines (Roman Catholic--Dominican Fathers)
  1611.
  Library: 1611, 21, OB, 200,000-___, E, LC, SC,
  673-425, Fi Sl Mi Pi Ma Mu VF   373
SEMINARY OF OUR LADY OF THE MOST HOLY

Taiwan (Republic of China) (cont.)
    Taiwan (Lutheran Church--Missouri Synod) 1952.
    Library: 1952, 2, OS, 8,000-5,000, Chinese E,
    DDC, 43-22, Sl Mu   389
TAIWAN CONSERVATIVE BAPTIST THEOLOGICAL
    SEMINARY. Box 3, Hsi Lo, Taiwan (Conserva-
    tive Baptists) 1957.   390
YU-SHAN THEOLOGICAL INSTITUTE. Lee-Yu,
    Shou-Feng, Hualien, Taiwan (Presbyterian) 1946.   391
HOLY LIGHT BIBLE SEMINARY. Box 270, Kaohsiung,
    Taiwan (Methodist) 1955.   392
CENTRAL TAIWAN THEOLOGICAL COLLEGE. P.O.
    Box 74, Taichung, Taiwan (Holiness Church, Oriental
    Missionary Society) 1951.   393
TAIWAN LUTHERAN THEOLOGICAL SEMINARY. 13
    Lane 241, Ta Ya Road, Taichung, Taiwan (Lutheran
    Church of Taiwan) 1957.   394
TRUE JESUS THEOLOGICAL SEMINARY. Taichung,
    Taiwan (True Jesus Church) 1963.   395
TAINAN THEOLOGICAL COLLEGE. 228 Tung Men
    Road, Tainan, Taiwan (Episcopal Church in Taiwan,
    Methodist Church in Taiwan, Theological Education
    Fund, Foundation of Theological Education) 1876.
    Library: 1876, 1, OB, OS, 50,000-20,000, Chinese
    E, UTS, F-S, 132-56, Fi Sl Ma VF   396
MISSION OF THE CHRISTIAN REFORMED CHURCH.
    No. 19, Alley 8, Lane 133, Nanking Road, Section 4,
    Taipei, Taiwan, 1961.
    Calvin Library: 1961, 0, OB, OS, ___-956, Chinese
    E, Decimal, F-S, 3-0, Sl Ma   397
NAZARENE THEOLOGICAL COLLEGE. Box 936,
    Taipei, Taiwan (Church of the Nazarene) 1958.   398
TAIWAN BAPTIST THEOLOGICAL SEMINARY. P.O.
    Box 427, Taipei, Taiwan (Baptist, Southern Baptist
    F.M.B.--American, Taiwan Biu) 1952.   399
TAIWAN MISSIONARY COLLEGE. Chi Chang, Hsin
    Tien, Taipei, Taiwan (Seventh Day Adventists Far
    Eastern Division, South China Island Union) 1942.
    Library: 1942, 1, OB, 5,908-5,908, Chinese E,
    DDC, F-S, 43-6, Fi Sl Pi Ma Mu   400
TAO SENG THEOLOGICAL COLLEGE. 74 Ta-Tun Zi,
    Hsin-pei-Tou, Taipei Hsien, Taiwan (Tao Seng Theo-
    logical College Association--Living Way) 1956.   401
TAIWAN THEOLOGICAL COLLEGE. 2-Yungfu, Shilin
    Chen, Taipei Shian, Taiwan (Presbyterian Church of
    Formosa) 1882.   402

Thailand
THAILAND BAPTIST THEOLOGICAL SEMINARY. P.O.
  Box 832, Bangkok, Thailand (Baptist, F.M.B. of
  Southern Baptist Convention--American) 1952.   403
THAILAND THEOLOGICAL SEMINARY.   Box
  37, Chiengmai, Thailand (Theological Education Fund,
  Foundation for Theological Education S.E.A. and
  T.T.S.) 1888.
  Library: 1949, 2, OS, 10,000-8,000, E, DDC, SC,
  12-12, Ma VF   404

Turkey
ANKARA UNIVERSITY FACULTY OF THEOLOGY.
  Ankara, Turkey, 1946.   405
THEOLOGICAL SCHOOL OF HALKI. Halki, Turkey
  (Greek Orthodox Church of Egypt, Greek Orthodox
  Church of Turkey) 1844.   406
RUM TAHIPLER OKNTRE. Istanbul, Turkey (Eastern
  Orthodox).   •   407

Bahamas
BAHAMAS BAPTIST INSTITUTE. P. O. Box 1644,
Nassau, Bahamas (Bahamas Southern Baptist Mis-
sion) 1957.
Library: 1957, 1, OS, ___-2,500, E, DDC, 5-0   408

Barbados
CODRINGTON COLLEGE. Barbados, West Indies
(Anglican) 1830.
Library: 1830, 0, OB, OS, 10,000-10,000, E,
Author-Subject, SC, 12-0   409

Cuba
SEMINARIO "EL BUEN PASTOR." Arroyo Arenas,
Havana, Cuba (Roman Catholic).   410
SEMINARIO TEOLOGICO BAUTISTA DE CUBA OCCI-
DENTAL. Apartado 1457, Jesus del Monte, Havana,
Cuba (Baptist) 1935.   411
SEMINARIO EVANGELICO DE TEOLOGIA. Apartado
149, Matanzas, Cuba (Anglican, Methodist, Presby-
terian) 1946.   412
SEMINARIO TEOLOGICO BAUTISTA DE CUBA ORI-
ENTAL. Apartado 731, Santiago de Cuba, Cuba
(Baptist--American Baptist Convention) 1949.   413

Dominican Republic
SEMINARIO PONTIFICO "ST. THOMAS DE AQUINO."
Avenida Cordell Hull, Apartado 83, Ciudad Trujillo,
Dominican Republic (Roman Catholic).   414
SEMINARIO BIBLICO. Santiago, Dominican Republic
(Free Methodist) 1927.   415

Haiti
SEMINAIRE THEOLOGIQUE BAPTISTE D'HAITI. Box
40, Cap Haitien, Haiti (American Baptist Home Mission Society, Valley Forge, Pennsylvania) 1947.
Bibliotheque Margaret Karpe: 1947, 3, OB, OS,
4,000-2,500, E F, DDC, 8-0   416

GRAND SEMINAIRE. Casille Postale 278, Port-au-
Prince, Haiti (Roman Catholic).   417
SEMINAIRE DE THEOLOGIE. Box 802, Montronis,
Port-au-Prince, Haiti (Episcopal U.S.A.) 1947.   418

Jamaica
CALABAR THEOLOGICAL COLLEGE. 61 Red Hill
Road, Half-way Tree, Kingston, Jamaica (Baptist),
1843.   419
JAMAICA THEOLOGICAL SEMINARY. 14 West Avenue,
Kingston 8, Jamaica (Missionary Church Association)
1962.
Library: 1962, 1, OS, 4,000-3,000, E, DDC, 12-0 420
JAMAICAN SCHOOL OF THEOLOGY. 37 Hope Road,
Half-way Tree, Kingston 10, Jamaica (Church of
God) 1926.   421
UNITED THEOLOGICAL COLLEGE OF THE WEST
INDIES. P.O. Box 136, Kingston 7, Jamaica (Eleven
church bodies in the Caribbean area) 1966.
Library: 1966, 1, OB, OS, 20,000-6,000, E, UTS,
25-0   422
WEST INDIES COLLEGE. Mandeville, Jamaica (Seventh
Day Adventist) 1919.   423
BETHEL BIBLE COLLEGE. Carron Hall P.O., St.
Mary, Jamaica (Church of God--Cleveland, Tennes-
see) 1943.
Library: 1960, 0, OB, OS, 576-487, E, DDC,
F-S, 1-1   424

Puerto Rico
INSTITUTO BIBLICO MENONITA. Apartado 146, Aibo-
nito, Puerto Rico (Mennonite) 1954.   425
DOMINICAN SEMINARY. J-Street, P.O. Box 1968,
Reparto Flamingo, Bayamon, Puerto Rico (Padres
Dominicos de Puerto Rico, Inc.) 1960.
Biblioteca Central de los Padres Dominicos de
Puerto Rico: 1960, 1, OB, OS, 42,000-16,987,
E S, own, 108-22   426
EL SEMINARIO EPISCOPAL DEL CARIBE. Box 757,
Caroline, Puerto Rico 00630 (Episcopal Church)
1961.
Library: 1961, 2, OB, OS, ___-15,000, E F S,
LC, 150-130, Ar Mi Mu VF   427
SEMINARIO EVANGELICO DE PUERTO RICO. P.O.
Box C, Rio Piedras, Puerto Rico 00928 (Six de-
nominations) 1919.
Biblioteca "Juan de Valdes": 1958, OS, 75,000-

Puerto Rico (cont.)
16,000, E, UTS, SC, 145-20, Sl Mi Pi Ma VF   428
SEMINARIO TEOLOGICO DEFENSORES DE LA FE.
P.O. Box 203, Rio Piedras, Puerto Rico (Defenders
of the Faith) 1945.   429
INTERAMERICAN BIBLE INSTITUTE. Box 411, Saint
Just, Puerto Rico.   430

Trinidad
ARCHDIOCESAN SEMINARY OF ST. JOHN VIANNEY
AND THE AFRICAN MARTYRS. Mt. St. Benedict,
Tunapuna, British West Indies, Trinidad (Roman
Catholic).   431
CARIBBEAN UNION COLLEGE. P.O. Box 175, Port-
of-Spain, Trinidad (Seventh Day Adventist) 1927. 432
OPEN BIBLE INSTITUTE. Box 82, San Fernando,
Trinidad or 8-14 Efforts West, San Fernando, Trini-
dad (Open Bible Standard Churches, Inc.) 1956.
Library: 1957, 0, OS, 10,000-1,700, E, DDC, F-
S, 5-0, Sl   433
ST. ANDREW'S THEOLOGICAL COLLEGE. P.O. Box
92, San Fernando, Trinidad (Presbyterian Church in
Trinidad and Granada) 1892.
Library: 1892, 1, OS, 4,500-3,800, E, UTS, 6-___,
Ar   434

Central America

British Honduras
INSTITUTO BIBLICO DE NAZAREEN. Benque Viejo,
British Honduras (Church of the Nazarene) 1950.   435

Costa Rica
ESCUELA DE PREPARACION DE OBREROS METOD-
ISTAS. Apartado 78, Alajuela, Costa Rica (Method-
ist) 1957.   436
INSTITUTO TEOLOGICO BAUTISTA. Apartado 1883,
San Jose, Costa Rica (Baptist) 1951.   437
SEMINARIO BIBLICO LATINOAMERICANO. Apartado
901, San Jose, Costa Rica (Latin America Mission,
Inc.) 1923.
Biblioteca Memorial Enrique Strachan: 1938, 1, OB,
OS, 11,000-10,079, E S, UTS, F-S, SC, 69-0, Ma   438
SEMINARIO CENTRAL. Apartado 2267, San Jose,
Costa Rica (Costa Rican Catholic Province) 1866.
Library: 1866, 1, OB, OS, 6,000-6,000, G S, Sub-
ject, F-S, SC, 6-0   439
CENTRO DE ESTUDIOS TEOLOGICOS. Iglesia Santa
Maria, Squirres, Costa Rica (Anglican) 1964.   440

El Salvador
SEMINARIO CENTRAL "ST. JOSE-DE-LA-MONTANA."
Apartado 78, San Salvador, El Salvador (Roman
Catholic).   441
COLEGIO I.B.I.D.C.A. Apartado 1775, Santa Tecla,
El Salvador (Church of God) 1946.   442

Guatemala
WILLIAMSON BIBLE INSTITUTE. Apartado 11, Coban,
Alta Verapaz, Guatemala (Church of the Nazarene,
Department of World Missions) 1950.
Library: 1950, 1, OB, OS, 4,000-2,000, S, Memory-
o-matic, F-S, 8-0, Sl Pi Ma Mu   443
INSTITUTO BIBLICO BEREA. Mision Amigos, Apartado
8, Chiquimula, Guatemala (California Yearly Meeting
of Friends) 1921.

Guatemala (cont.)
  Library: 1921, 1, OS, 1,500-1,300, S, DDC,
  F-S, 5-4   444
INSTITUTO BIBLICO CENTROAMERICANO. Apartado
  213, Guatemala, Guatemala (Central American Mis-
  sion).   445
INSTITUTO SUPERIOR TEOLOGICO BAUTISTA.
  Apartado 322, Guatemala, Guatemala (Convencion
  Bautista de Guatemala).
  Library: 1, OB, OS, 5,000-1,980, S, DDC, F-S,
  22-14, Ma Mu   446
SEMINARIO EVANGELICO PRESBITERIANO. San Felipe,
  Reu., Guatemala (Iglesia Nacional Presbiteriana de
  Guatemala) 1935.
  Library: 1935, 1, 10,000-5,000, E S, own, F-S,
  5-0   447
INSTITUTO BIBLICO BAUTISTA "PABLO BELL."
  c/o M. J. Ledbetter--Director, Panajachel, Solola,
  Guatemala (Baptist) 1962.   448

Honduras
THEOLOGICAL INSTITUTE. Apartado No. 17, San
  Pedro Sula, Honduras (El Sinodo Evangelico y
  Reformado, The United Church Board for World
  Ministries of the United Church of Christ) 1962.
  Library: 1962, 0, OS, 4,000-1,500, S, UTS, F-
  S, 29-14, Fi Sl Pi Mu   449
SEMINARIO INTERDIOCESANO "SAN JOSE." Teguci-
  galpa, Honduras (Roman Catholic).   450
TEOLOGICA BAUTISTA. Apartado 279, Tegucigalpa
  D. C., Honduras (Southern Baptist F.M.B., Mision
  Bautista de Honduras) 1959.
  Library: 1964, 1, OB, OS, 5,000-2,000, S, DDC,
  F-S, SC, 15-0, Fi Pi Ma Mu   451

Mexico
SEMINARIO CONCILIAR. Jardinez de la Cruz, Aguas-
  calientes, Mexico (Roman Catholic).   452
MAJOR SEMINARY. Apartado No. 616, Chihuahua,
  Chihuahua, Mexico (Roman Catholic).   453
SEMINARIO CONCILIAR. Apartado Postal 38, Colima,
  Mexico (Roman Catholic)   454
SEMINARIO TEOLOGICO PRESBITERIANO DE MEXICO.
  Aba-Solo 18, Coyoacan 21, District Federal, Mexico
  (Presbyterian) 1897.   455
SEMINARIO CONCILIAR. Apartado Postal 24, Culiacan,
  Mexico (Roman Catholic).   456

SEMINARIO CONCILIAR. Zarco 311 NTE, Durango,
  Mexico (Roman Catholic).   457
SEMINARIO CONCILIAR. Apartado Postal 244, Guada-
  lajara, Mexico (Roman Catholic).   458
INSTITUTO BIBLICO BEREA. Matamoros y Durango,
  Hermosillo, Sonora, Mexico (Church of God).   459
SEMINARIO CONCILIAR. Hermosillo, Mexico (Roman
  Catholic).   460
SEMINARIO CONCILIAR. Calle de Guadalupe, Huajua-
  pan de Leon, Oxoaca, Mexico (Roman Catholic).   461
SEMINARIO CONCILIAR. Apartado 3, Huejutla (HGO),
  Mexico (Roman Catholic).   462
SEMINARIO CONCILIAR. Mina 39, Jacona, Michoacan,
  Mexico (Roman Catholic).   463
SEMINARIO CONCILIAR. Ursula Galvan 82, Apartado
  79, Jalapa, Vera Cruz, Mexico (Roman Catholic).   464
SEMINARIO CONCILIAR. Merida 405, Leon (GTO),
  Mexico (Roman Catholic).   465
SEMINARIO CONCILIAR. Calle 18, No. 78 Itzimna,
  Merida, Yucatan, Mexico (Roman Catholic).   466
CENTRO DE ESTUDIOS TEOLOGICO AUGSBURGO.
  Apartado 20-416, Mexico City 20, D. F., Mexico
  (Lutheran) 1965.   467
CENTRO EVANGELICO UNIDO. Apartado 117 bix,
  Mexico City 1, D. F., Mexico (Methodist, Christian,
  Congregational) 1917.
  Biblioteca G. Wallace: 1917, 1, OB, OS, ___-10,000,
  S E, DDC, F-S, 75-10, Pi Ma VF   468
SEMINARIO CONCILIAR. Moneda 2, Esq. Abasolo,
  Mexico City, Mexico (Roman Catholic).   469
SEMINARIO SAN ANDRES. La Otra Banda 40, Mexico
  City 20, D. F., Mexico (Anglican).   470
SEMINARIO CONCILIAR. Eduardo Ruiz 20, Apartado
  58, Morelia, Michoacan, Mexico (Roman Catholic).   471
SEMINARIO CONCILIAR. Garcia Vigil 40, Oaxaca,
  Oaxaca, Mexico (Roman Catholic).   472
SEMINARIO CONCILIAR 9 Oriente No. 5, Apartado 281,
  Pueblo, Mexico (Roman Catholic).   473
SEMINARIO CONCILIAR. Apartado Postal 49, Quere-
  taro, Mexico (Roman Catholic).   474
SEMINARIO TEOLOGICO PRESBITERIANO A. R. DE
  MEXICO. Apartado 20, Rio Verde, S. L. P., Mexico
  (Iglesia Presbiteriano A. R. de Mexico) 1954-1965.
  Halliday Library: 1954, 0, OB, OS, 10,000-6,000,
  E S, Decimal, SC, 8-0, Fi Sl Mu   475
SEMINARIO CONCILIAR DE SAN LUIS POTOSI. Ave-
  nida de la Paz 180, San Luis Potosi, S. L. P., Mexi-

Mexico (cont.)
    co (Seminario Conciliar Guadlupano Josefino)
    1855.
    Library: 1855, 0, 12,000-12,000, Vatican, 78-0,
    Ma   476
SEMINARIO CONCILIAR.   Apartado 423, Tampico,
    Mexico (Roman Catholic).   477
SEMINARIO CONCILIAR.   Apartado 226, Tijuana, Baja
    California, Mexico (Roman Catholic).   478
SEMINARIO BAUTISTA DE MEXICO.   San Fernando 49,
    Tialpan 22, D.F. , Mexico (American Baptist Home
    Mission Societies) 1946.
    Library: 1946, 0, OS, 10,000-6,000, E S, DDC,
    F-S, 2-0, Mu   479
SEMINARIO CONCILIAR.   Apartado 82, Toluca, Mexico
    (Roman Catholic).   480
SEMINARIO TEOLOGICO BAUTISTA MEXICANO.
    Apartado 320, Torreon, Coahuila, Mexico (F.M.B.
    of the Southern Baptist Convention) 1901.
    Biblioteca Dr. Alejandro Trevino: 1901, 1, OB, OS,
    15,000-6,500, S, DDC, F-S, 62-8, Ma Mu VF   481
SEMINARIO CONCILIAR.   Miguel Auza 13, Apartado
    131, Zacatecas, Mexico (Roman Catholic).   482

Nicaragua
INSTITUTO BIBLICO MORAVO.   Bilwaskarma, Nicaragua
    (Moravian) 1930.   483
INSTITUTO TEOLOGICO BAUTISTA.   Apartado 2555,
    Managua, Nicaragua (Baptist Convention of Nica-
    ragua; American Baptist Home Mission Society, Valley
    Forge, Pennsylvania) 1965.
    Library: 1965, 0, OB, 5,000-1,300, S, DDC, F-S,
    6-0, Ar Ma   484
SEMINARIO NACIONAL.   Managua, Nicaragua (Roman
    Catholic).   485

Panama
SEMINARIO TEOLOGICO BAUTISTA DE PANAMA.   Box
    7242, Panama, Panama (Baptist) 1955.   486

Belgium

RUUSBROEC-GENOOTSCHAP. Printsstraat 17,
Antwerp 1, Belgium (Ruusbroec-Genootschap)
1925.

Library: 1925, 1, 150,000-60,000, own, SC,
110-   498
GRAND SEMINAIRE. 72 rue de la Potterie, Bruges,
Belgium (Roman Catholic).   499
FACULTE UNIVERSITAIRE "SAINT LOUIS." 38 Boule-
vard du Jardin Bontanique, Brussels, Belgium (Roman
Catholic) 1858.   500
SEMINAIRE SAINT PAUL. Drongen, Belgium (Roman
Catholic).
Biblioteek Oude Abdij.   501
BIBLIOTHEQUE DES DOMINICANS. 41 rue Haute,
Ghent, Belgium (Roman Catholic).   502
GRAND SEMINAIRE. Keep 1, Ghent, Belgium (Roman
Catholic) 1650.
Library: 1650, 2, OB, OS, 15,000-10,000, Flem-
ish F L, own, F-S, SC, 100-100   503
SINT JAN BERCHMANSCOLLEGE. Waversebaan 220,
Heverlee, Belgium (Roman Catholic--Noord Belgische
Provicie S. J.) 1839.
Bibliotheek S. J. Leuven, Sectie: 1839, 3, OB,
500,000-350,000, D, own, SC, 800-   504
SINT JAN BERCHMANSCOLLEGE--CENTRUM VOOR
KERKELIJKE STUDIES. Waversebaan 220, Heverlee,
Belgium (Roman Catholic--Noord Belgische Provicie
S. J.).   505
GRAND SEMINAIRE. Rue de Premontres, Liege, Bel-
gium (Roman Catholic).   506
S. J. SAINT-ALBERT. 95, St. Jansbergsteenweg,
Louvain, Belgium (Roman Catholic) 1839.
Library: 1940, 3, OB, OS, 650,000-350,000, F,
own, 800-   507
UNIVERSITE CATHOLIQUE DE LOUVAIN--FACULTY
OF THEOLOGY. 4, rue Kraeken, Louvain, Belgium
(Roman Catholic) 1425.   508
SEMINAIRE SAINT JOSEPH. 139 Yzerveed, Malines,
Belgium (Roman Catholic).   509
GROOT SEMINARIE MECHELEN-BRUSSEL. 18 de
Merodestraat, Mechelen, Belgium (Roman Catholic)
1595.
Library: 1808, 2, OB, 100,000-100,000, D F, own,
SC, 187-___, Ar Sl Mi   510
GRAND SEMINAIRE. Namur, Belgium (Roman Catho-
lic).   511

STUDIEHUIS DER MINDERBROEDERS. 5 Minder-
broedestraat, Sint-Truiden, Belgium (Roman
Catholic).
Bibliotheek van ket Theologisch. 512
SEMINAIRE EPISCOPAL. 28 rue des Jesuites,
Tournai, Belgium (Roman Catholic) 1808.
Library: 1808, 1, OB, ___-50,000, F L, F-S, SC,
135-___, Ar 513

Bulgaria
ST. JOHN OF RITA THEOLOGICAL SEMINARY. Gara
Cherepish, Bulgaria (Greek Orthodox--Patriarchate
of Bulgaria). 514
DUCHOVNA ACADEMIA--ST. CLEMENT OF OCHRIDA
THEOLOGICAL ACADEMY. P. Lenin No. 19, Sofia,
Bulgaria (Eastern Orthodox and Bulgarian Patri-
archate). 515
SOFIISKINYA DARZHAVEN U. Bul. Ruski 15, Sofia,
Bulgaria.
Biblioteka Kam Spetziyalnost "Filosofia." 516

Czechoslovakia, Socialist Republic of
SLOWAKISCHE EVANGELISCHE THEOLOGISCHE FACUL-
TAT. Konventna 11, Bratislava, Czechoslovakia
(Lutheran). 517
UNIVERSITY OF PRAGUE--COMENIUS FACULTY OF
THEOLOGY. Knikovna, Jungman nova 9, Prague,
Czechoslovakia (Reformed). 518
THEOLOGICAL FACULTY OF THE ORTHODOX CHURCH
IN PRAGUE. Sladkovicova 23, Slovakia, Presox,
Czechoslovakia (Greek Orthodox Church). 519

Denmark
AARHUS UNIVERSITET--FACULTY OF THEOLOGY.
Aarhus, Denmark, 1928. 520
NIELS STEENSENS BIBLIOTEK. Bredgade 69, Copen-
hagen, Denmark. 521
SAINT ANDREAS BIBLIOTEK. Kollegievej 2, Charlot-
tenlund, Copenhagen, Denmark. 522
KØBENHAVNS UNIVERSITET--TEOLOGISK LABORA-
TORIUM. Studiestraede 6, Copenhagen, Denmark,
1903.
Library: 1903, 1, OB, OS, 25,000-25,000, F-S,
25-25 523
UNIVERSITETS INSTITUT FOR DANSK KIRKEHIS-
TOIRE. Vodroffsvej 8, Copenhagen V, Denmark. 524
DANISH BAPTIST UNION SEMINARY. Tølløse, Den-

Denmark (cont.)
mark (Danish Baptist Union) 1967.   525

England
ST. AIDAN'S COLLEGE.   Birkenhead, Cheshire, Eng-
land (Anglican) 1847.
Library: 1847, 3, OB, OS, 10,000-3,000, E, DDC,
SC, 23-10   526
HANDSWORTH COLLEGE.   Birmingham 20, England
(Methodist) 1881.
Library: 1881, 1, OB, OS, 13,000-18,000, own, SC,
40-10   527
OVERDALE COLLEGE.   Bristol Road, Selly Oak,
Birmingham, England (Churches of Christ--Dis-
ciples) 1920.
Overdale College Library and Historical Library
Annexe: 1920, 0, OB, OS, 6,000-5,500, E, DDC,
SC, 10-1   528
THE QUEEN'S COLLEGE.   Somerset Road, Edgbaston,
Birmingham, 15, England (The Church of England)
1828.
Library: 1928, 0, OB, OS, 17,000-17,000, E, DDC,
F-S, 51-51   529
UNIVERSITY OF BIRMINGHAM--DEPARTMENT OF
THEOLOGY.   Birmingham, England (Anglican) 1900. 530
UNIVERSITY OF BIRMINGHAM--INSTITUTE FOR SHAPE
OF WORSHIP AND RELIGIOUS ARCHITECTURE.
Birmingham, England (Anglican) 1962.   531
ANGLICAN THEOLOGICAL COLLEGE.   Tyndale Hall,
Pembroke Road, Bristol 8, England (Bible Church-
man's Missionary Society) 1927.
Library: 1927, 0, OB, OS, 15,000-10,000, E, own,
23-23   532
CLIFTON THEOLOGICAL COLLEGE.   14-26 Stoke Hill,
Stoke Bishop, Bristol 9, England (Anglican) 1932.
Library: 1932, 3, OB, OS, 10,000-6,000, E, Black-
well Theological Catalog, F-S, 20-6   533
UNIVERSITY OF BRISTOL--BRISTOL BAPTIST COL-
LEGE.   1679 Woodland Road, Bristol, England (Bap-
tist) 1679.   534
WESLEY COLLEGE.   Wenbury Hill, Westbury-on-Trym,
Bristol, England (Methodist Church of Great Britain)
1842.
Library: 1842, 0, OS, ____-23,000, DDC, SC, 25-
10   535
RIDLEY HALL.   Cambridge, England (Anglican) 1879. 536
WESLEY HOUSE.   Jesus Lane, Cambridge, England

(Methodist) 1921.
Library: 1921, 0, OB, OS, 15,000-12,000, E,
Card, F-S, SC, 12-4   537
WESTCOTT HOUSE. Jesus Lane, Cambridge, England
(Anglican) 1881.
Chase Library: 1926, 0, OB, OS, 12,000-10,000,
E, own, F-S, 30-20   538
BISHOPS' COLLEGE. Churchgate, Cheshunt, Hertford-
shire, England (Anglican) 1909.
Library: 1909, 0, OS, 15,000-10,000, E, Shelf,
F-S, SC, 6-‾‾   539
THEOLOGICAL ‾COLLEGE. Chichester, England (Ang-
lican) 1839.   540
THEOLOGICAL COLLEGE. Cuddeston, England (Ang-
lican) 1854.   541
THE COLLEGE. Durham, England (Church of England--
The Trustees of Nathaniel, Lord Crewe, Bishop of
Durham) 1832.
The Archdeacon Sherp Library: 1778, 2, OS,
6,000-5,000, E, DDC   542
THE DEAN AND CHAPTER OF DURHAM CATHEDRAL.
The College, Durham, England (Church of England)
995.
The Dean and Chapter Library: 635, 2, OS, 30,000-
30,000, E L, Fixed Location, SC, 20-10, Ar Sl Mi
Pi Ma Mu   543
ST. CHAD'S COLLEGE. Durham, England (Anglican)
1904.   544
ST. CUTHBERT'S SEMINARY. Ushaw, Durham, Eng-
land (Roman Catholic) 1871.   545
ST. JOHN'S COLLEGE. Durham, England (Independent)
1909.
Library: 1909, 0, OB, OS, 10,000-6,500, E, DDC,
F-S, 15-‾‾   546
HEYTHORP ‾COLLEGE. Chipping Norton, Oxon, Hey-
thorp, England (Roman Catholic--Society of Jesus)
1926.   547
UNIVERSITY OF LEEDS--COLLEGE OF THE RESUR-
RECTION. Mirfield, Yorkshire, Leeds, England
(Anglican) 1909.   548
LICHFIELD THEOLOGICAL COLLEGE. Lichfield, Eng-
land (Church of England) 1857.
Library: 1857, 0, OS, 11,500-10,500, E, DDC,
F-S, 10-2   549
LINCOLN THEOLOGICAL COLLEGE. Drury Lane,
Lincoln, England (Church of England) 1881.
Library: 1881, 4, OS, ___'-4,500, E, own,

England (cont.)
   F-S, 20-9   550
FRIENDS HOUSE.   Euston Road, London N.W.I., Eng-
   land (London Yearly Meeting of the Religious Society
   of Friends) 1673.
   Library of the Society of Friends: 1673, 3, OB,
   OS, ___-100,000, E, own, SC, Ar Sl Mi Pi Ma   551
KING'S COLLEGE LONDON.   Strand, London WC 2,
   England (Anglican) 1829.
   Library: 1831, 2, OB, ___-17,000, E, LC, F-S,
   SC, 74-50   552
LEO BAECK COLLEGE.   33 Seymour Place, London
   W 1, England (Reformed Judaism).   553
SOUTHWARK ORDINATION HOUSE.   16 Duke at Hill,
   London S.C. 1, England (Anglican) 1965.   554
UNIVERSITY COLLEGE.   Gower Street, London, Eng-
   land (Jewish) 1826.   555
UNIVERSITY OF LONDON--NEW COLLEGE.   527
   Finchley Road, London W.C. 2, England (Congrega-
   tional) 1637.   556
UNIVERSITY OF LONDON--SPURGEON'S COLLEGE.
   South Norwood Hill, London S.E. 25, England (Free
   Churches) 1856.   557
HARTLEY VICTORIA COLLEGE.   40 Spring Bridge
   Road, Manchester 16, England (Methodist) 1881.
   Library: 1881, 1, OB, OS, ___-17,000, E, F-S,
   SC, 26-18   558
VICTORIA UNIVERSITY OF MANCHESTER.   Oxford
   Road, Manchester 13, England (Independent) 1880.   559
NEWCASTLE UNIVERSITY--DIVINITY DEPARTMENT.
   Newcastle upon Tyne, England (Independent) 1963.   560
HOUSE OF THE SACRED MISSION.   Kelham, Newark,
   Nottinghamshire, England (Anglican) 1893.
   Library: 1893, 1, OS, 40,000-35,500, E, DDC,
   F-S, 40-30   561
' LONDON COLLEGE OF DIVINITY.   Green Lane,
   Northwood, Middlesex, England (Church of England)
   1863.
   Library: 1863, 0, OB, OS, 12,000-11,000, E,
   own, F-S, 14-2   562
UNIVERSITY OF NOTTINGHAM--DIVINITY FACULTY.
   Nottingham, England, 1881.   563
MANSFIELD COLLEGE.   Oxford, England (Congrega-
   tional) 1869.
   Library: 1869, 1, OB, OS, 20,000-20,000, E, own,
   F-S, SC, 85-70, VF   564
RIPON HALL.   Oxford, England (Anglican) 1898.   565

ST. STEPHEN'S HOUSE. Oxford, England, 1876.
  Library: 1876, 0, OS, 6,000-5,000, E, own,
  F-S, 4-4   566
UNIVERSITY OF OXFORD--CHRIST CHURCH. Oxford,
  England (Roman Catholic) 1525.
  Library: 1563, 3, OB, OS, 100,000-25,000, E,
  F-S, SC, 7-7, Ar Mu   567
UNIVERSITY OF OXFORD--REGENT'S PARK, Oxford,
  England (Baptist) 1810.   568
UNIVERSITY OF OXFORD--SAINT BENET'S HALL.
  38 Gates Street, Oxford, England (Roman Catholic)
  1899.   569
UNIVERSITY OF OXFORD--WORCESTER COLLEGE.
  Oxford, England (Roman Catholic) 1238.   570
WYCLIFFE HALL. Oxford, England (Anglican) 1877.   571
THEOLOGICAL COLLEGE. Rochester, England (Angli-
  can) 1959.   572
SALISBURY THEOLOGICAL COLLEGE. 19 The Close,
  Salisbury, Wiltshire, England (Anglican) 1860.
  Library: 1860, 0, OB, OS, 20,000-15,000, E,
  Simple Card, F-S, 8-8   573
OAKS HILL THEOLOGICAL COLLEGE. Southgate N
  14, England (Anglican) 1932.   574
UNIVERSITY OF SOUTHAMPTON. Highfield, Southampton,
  England (Jewish) 1952.   575
ST. JOHN'S SEMINARY. Wonersh, NR Guildford, Sur-
  rey, England (Roman Catholic--The Archdiocese of
  Southward, England) 1891.
  Library: 1891, 4, OB, OS, ___-20,000, E, UDC,
  F-S, SC, 35-8   576
UNIVERSITY OF LONDON--RICHMOND COLLEGE.
  Richmond, Surrey, England (Methodist) 1886.   577
OSCOTT COLLEGE. Sutton Coldfield, Warwickshire,
  England (Roman Catholic) 1794.
  Library: 1794, 4, OB, OS, 50,000-40,000, E F L,
  DDC, SC, 25-20   578
ST. MARY'S COLLEGE. New Oscott, Sutton Coldfield,
  England (Roman Catholic).
  Library: SC   579
ST. EDMUND'S COLLEGE. Old Hall Green, Ware,
  Hertfordshire, England (Roman Catholic).   580
ST. BONIFACE COLLEGE. Warminster, Wiltshire,
  England (Anglican) 1871.   581
WELLS THEOLOGICAL COLLEGE. Wells, England
  (Church of England) 1840.
  Library: 1842, 1, OS, 14,000-9,000, E, Subject,
  F-S, 24-17   582

England (cont.)
UPHOLLAND COLLEGE.   Wigan, Lancashire, England
  (Roman Catholic) 1883.
  Library: 1883, 0, OB, OS, 20,000-15,000, E F L,
  DDC, F-S, SC, 25-25   583
WORCESTER ORDINATION COLLEGE.   Worcester,
  England (Anglican) 1952.   584

Finland
ABO AKADEMI.   Abo 2, Finland (Evangelical Lutheran
  Church of Finland) 1924.
  Teologiska Institutionens Bibliotek: 1924, 1, OB, OS,
    -26,000, E G Swedish, own, F-S, 100-100, Mu   585
UNIVERSITY OF HELSINKI--FACULTY OF THEOLOGY.
  Fabianinkatu 33, Helsinki 17, Finland, 1640.
  Library: 1902, 4, OS, 30,000-25,000, E G, UDC,
  276-230, Sl Mi Ma   586
SUOMEN ORTODOKSINEN PAPPISSEMINARII.   Suokatu
  41, Kuopio, Finland (Eastern Orthodox).   587

France
GRAND SEMINAIRE.   7, Cours de la Trinite, Aix
  (Bouches-du-Rhone) France (Roman Catholic).   588
GRAND SEMINAIRE.   14, rue de la Republique, Albi
  (Tarn) France (Roman Catholic).   589
GRAND SEMINAIRE.   61, rue St. Francisien, Amiens
  (Somme) France (Roman Catholic).   590
GRAND SEMINAIRE.   36, rue Barra, Angers (Maine et
  Loire) France (Roman Catholic).   591
UNIVERSITE CATHOLIQUE DE L'OUEST.   Angers,
  France, 1875.   592
PIERRE AUMAITRE CENTER.   Route de Bordeaux, 16
  Angouleme, France, 1905.
  Library: 1905, 1, OB, OS, 10,000-7,000, F, Sub-
  ject, 10-5   593
GRAND SEMINAIRE.   Montee de Tresum, Annecy -
  74 (Haute-Savoie) France (Roman Catholic) 1600.
  Library: 1660, 1, OB, 50,000-50,000, F, Subject,
  SC, 40-40, Ar   594
GRAND SEMINAIRE "NOTRE DAME."   Argenton (Indre)
  France (Roman Catholic).   595
GRAND SEMINAIRE.   103, rue d'Amiens, Arras (Pas-
  de-Calais) France (Roman Catholic).   596
GRAND SEMINAIRE.   Auch (Gers) France (Roman
  Catholic).   597
GRAND SEMINAIRE.   17, rue St. Antoine, Autun (Saone
  et Loire) France (Roman Catholic).   598

GRAND SEMINAIRE. Rue Champfeu, 03 Avenue,
Avermes (Allier) France (Roman Catholic) 1800.   599
GRAND SEMINAIRE "ST. CHARLES." Avignon
(Vaucluse) France (Roman Catholic).   600
GRAND SEMINAIRE. Rue Nesmond, Bayeux (Calvados)
France (Roman Catholic).   601
GRAND SEMINAIRE. Bayonne (Basses-Pyrenees)
France (Roman Catholic).   602
GRAND SEMINAIRE. 101, rue de la Madeleine,
Beauvais (Oise) France (Roman Catholic).   603
GRAND SEMINAIRE "ST. ANTHELME." Belley (Ain)
France (Roman Catholic).   604
GRAND SEMINAIRE DE BESANCON. 20, rue Megevand,
25 - Besancon, France (Roman Catholic) 1680.
Library: 1680, 0, OB, 40,000-40,000, F, A-Z by
author, F-S, 80-___   605
GRAND SEMINAIRE. 1, rue de Berry, Blois (Loire-et-
Cher) France (Roman Catholic).   606
GRAND SEMINAIRE "NOTRE DAME DE VOIRONS."
Boege (Haute Savoie) France (Roman Catholic).   607
GRAND SEMINAIRE DE BORDEAUX. 135 rue Saint
Genes, Bordeaux, France (Roman Catholic) 1804.
Library: 1804, 1, OB, OS, 60,000-40,000, F L,
A-Z, F-S, SC, 50-20   608
GRAND SEMINAIRE. Bourges (Indre) France (Roman
Catholic).   609
GRAND SEMINAIRE. 8, rue Jean-Murat, Cahors (Lot)
France (Roman Catholic).   610
GRAND SEMINAIRE. 101, rue de Solesmes, Cambrai
(Nord) France (Roman Catholic).   611
GRAND SEMINAIRE. 5, rue Jericho, Chalons (Chalons
sur Marne) France (Roman Catholic).   612
GRAND SEMINAIRE RICHE-LIEU. Chamalieres (Puy
de Dome) France (Roman Catholic).   613
GRAND SEMINAIRE. Avenue Docteur-Desfrauxois,
Chambery (Savoie) France (Roman Catholic).   614
GRAND SEMINAIRE. 1, rue St. Emann, Chartres
(Eure-et-Loire) France (Roman Catholic).   615
GRAND SEMINAIRE. Coutances (Manche) France
(Roman Catholic).   616
GRAND SEMINAIRE. Crasville par Evreux, France
(Roman Catholic).   617
GRAND SEMINAIRE. Dax (Landes) France (Roman
Catholic).   618
GRAND SEMINAIRE "ST. JEAN." Digne (Basses-
Alpes) France (Roman Catholic).   619
GRAND SEMINAIRE. 9, Boulevard Voltaire, Dijon

France (cont.)
  (Cote-d'Or) France (Roman Catholic).   620
"LE SAULCHOR" INSTITUT PHILOSOPHIQUE ET
  THEOLOGIQUE. Etoilles par Soissy-Sur-Seine,
  France (Roman Catholic) 1868.   621
GRAND SEMINAIRE "ST. IRENE. " Frauchentta
  (Rhone) France (Roman Catholic).   622
GRAND SEMINAIRE. Gap (Hautes-Alpes) France
  (Roman Catholic).   623
GRAND SEMINAIRE DE LA CASTILLE. Par La
  Crau, France (Roman Catholic).   624
GRAND-SEMINAIRE DE GRENOBLE. 38 La Tronche
  (Isere) France (Roman Catholic) 1700.
  Library: 1800, 0, OB, OS, 35,000-25,000, F-S,
  29-   625
GRAND SEMINAIRE. Langres (Haute-Marne) France
  (Roman Catholic).   626
GRAND SEMINAIRE. 1, rue Jean-Mace, Laval (May-
  enne) France (Roman Catholic).   627
GRAND SEMINAIRE. 158, Avenue leon-Bollee, Le
  Mans (Sarthe) France (Roman Catholic).   628
GRAND SEMINAIRE. 4, rue St. George, Le Puy
  (Haute-Loire) France (Roman Catholic).   629
GRAND SEMINAIRE. L'Houmeau (Charente-Maritime)
  France (Roman Catholic).   630
FACULTES CATHOLIQUES DE LILLE. 60, Boulevard
  Vauban, Lille (Nord) France (Roman Catholic) 1875. 631
GRAND SEMINAIRE. 74, Hippolyte-Lefebvre, Lille 59
  (Nord) France (Roman Catholic) 1913.   632
SEMINAIRE ACADEMIQUE. 41, rue du Port, Lille
  (Nord) France (Roman Catholic) 1875.   633
GRAND SEMINAIRE. Limoges (Haute-Vienne) France
  (Roman Catholic).   634
GRAND SEMINAIRE "NOTRE DAME DE MONTCRET. "
  Lons-le-Saunier France (Roman Catholic).   635
GRAND SEMINAIRE. Lucon (Vendee) France (Roman
  Catholic).   636
FACULTE DE THEOLOGIE S. J. 4 Montee de Four-
  viere, 69 Lyon 5° France (Roman Catholic--Society
  of Jesus) 1858.
  Library: 1858, 2, OB, OS, 200,000-150,000, E F,
  Numerical, 120-___ , Fi   637
FACULTES CATHOLIQUES DE LYON. 25, rue du Plat,
  69-Lyon 2e, France (Roman Catholic) 1875.
  Library: 1875, 6, OB, OS, 150,000-120,000, F,
  own, SC, 400-400   638
SALOMON REINACH UNIVERSITE. 15 Quai Claude

Bernard, Lyon 69, France (Roman Catholic) 1936.   639

GRAND SEMINAIRE.   28, rue Paul-Coxe, St. Joseph,
Marseille XIV, France (Roman Catholic).   640

GRAND SEMINAIRE.   8, rue Chage, Meaux (Seine-et-
Marne) France (Roman Catholic).   641

GRAND SEMINAIRE.   Mende (Lozere) France (Roman
Catholic).   642

GRAND SEMINAIRE.   5, rue Asfeld, Metz (Moselle)
France (Roman Catholic).   643

GRAND SEMINAIRE.   Quai Montmurcat, Montauban
(Tarn-et-Garonne) France (Roman Catholic).   644

FACULTE THEOLOGIE PROTESTANTE.   Rue Louis
Perrier, Montpellier (Herault) France (Eglise
Reformee de France) 1809.
Library: 1809, 1, 80,000-60,000, E F G, Acces-
sion, SC, 200-___, Pi Ma   645

GRAND SEMINAIRE.   4, rue Montels, Montpellier
(Herault) France (Roman Catholic).   646

GRAND SEMINAIRE MOULINS.   Moulins (Allier) France
(Roman Catholic--Diocese of Moulins) 1927.
Library: 1850, OB, OS, 30,000-30,000, F, French
System, SC, 15-___, Ar   647

GRAND SEMINAIRE.   Rue du Cardinal Richard, Nantes
44, France (Roman Catholic).   648

GRAND SEMINAIRE.   2, rue St. Benin, Nevers, France
(Roman Catholic).   649

GRAND SEMINAIRE.   Nice (Alpes-Maritimes) France
(Roman Catholic).   650

GRAND SEMINAIRE.   4, rue Salomon-Reinach, 30-
Nimes, France (Roman Catholic--Diocese de Nimes`
1823.
Library: 1823, 1, OS, 20,000-15,000, F, Alpha-
Numeric, SC, 10-0, Ar Pi Ma   651

GRAND SEMINAIRE.   1, Cloitre St. Aignan, Orleans
(Loiret) France (Roman Catholic).   652

GRAND SEMINAIRE.   Pamiers, France (Roman Catholic).   653

ALLIANCE ISRAELITE UNIVERSELLE.   Paris 9e,
France (Jewish) 1860.   654

BIBLIOTHEQUE SLAVE.   3, rue de Sevres, Paris 7e,
France, 1856.   655

CENTRE NATIONAL DE PASTORALE LITURGIQUE ET
INSTITUT SUPERIEUR DE LITURGIE.   11, rue Per-
ronet, 92 Nevilly-sur-Seine, Paris, France (Roman
Catholic) 1943.
Library: 1943, 2, OS, ___-8,000, F, own,
250-___   656

France (cont.)
CENTRE PROTESTANT D'ETUDES ET DE DOCUMEN-
  TATION. 54, rue des Saints Peres, Paris 7e,
  France, 1945.   657
FACULTE LIBRE DE THEOLOGIE PROTESTANTE DE
  PARIS. 83, Boulevard Arago, Paris 14e, France,
  1905.   658
HISTOIRE DES RELIGIONS UNIVERSITE. 17, rue de
  loi Sorbonne, Paris 5e, France (Roman Catholic)
  1945.   659
INSTITUT CATHOLIQUE DE PARIS. 21, rue d'Assas,
  Paris 6, France (Roman Catholic) 1875.
  Library: 1875, 1, OS, 650,000-600,000, F, Size,
  SC, 250-___, Ar   660
INSTITUT DE THEOLOGIE ORTHODOXE. 93, rue de
  Crimee, Paris 19, France, 1925.
  Library: 1925, 1, 17,000-16,500, E F G Russian,
  own, F-S, 23-‾‾‾   661
INSTITUT INTERNATIONAL D'ETUDES HEBRAIQUES.
  20, rue Servandoni, Paris 6eme, France (World
  Union for Progressive Judaism) 1954.
  Library: 1954, 1, OB, 10,000-6,000, F Hebrew,
  own, F-S, 25-‾‾‾   662
MAISON DE LA BONNE PRESSE. 22 Cours Albert
  1e, Paris 8c, France (Roman Catholic) 1873.   663
SEMINAIRE DES POLONAIS. 5, rue des Irlandais,
  Paris V, France (Roman Catholic).   664
SEMINAIRE ISRAELITE. 9, rue Vauquelin, Paris V,
  France (Jewish) 1829, 1946.   665
SEMINAIRE ST. SULPICE. 6, rue du Regard, Paris
  VI, France (Roman Catholic).   666
VICTOR CONSENS UNIVERSITE. 47, rue des Ecoles,
  Paris 5e, France (Roman Catholic) 1887.   667
GRAND SEMINAIRE. 38, Avenue de Paris, Perigueux
  (Dordogne) France (Roman Catholic).   668
GRAND SEMINAIRE. Perpignau (Pyrenees-Orientales)
  France (Roman Catholic).   669
GRAND SEMINAIRE. 10, rue de la Trinite, Poitiers
  86, France (Roman Catholic).   670
GRAND SEMINAIRE. Quimper, France (Roman Catho-
  lic).   671
GRAND SEMINAIRE. Reims (Ardennes) France (Roman
  Catholic).   672
GRAND SEMINAIRE. 147, rue de Brest - 35 - Rennes,
  France (Roman Catholic--Diocese de Rennes) 1907.
  Library: 1907, 1, OB, OS, 100,000-35,000, F,
  A-Z, SC, 42-0, Pi Ma Mu   673

GRAND SEMINAIRE.   23, Boulevard Denis-Peuch,
   Rodez, France (Roman Catholic)   674
GRAND SEMINAIRE.   88, rue Champ-des-Oiseaux,
   Rouen, France (Roman Catholic).   675
GRAND SEMINAIRE.   Saint-Brieux (Cotes-du-Nord)
   France (Roman Catholic).   676
GRAND SEMINAIRE.   Saint Die (Vosges) France
   (Roman Catholic).   677
GRAND SEMINAIRE.   Saint Flour (Cantal) France
   (Roman Catholic).   678
GRAND SEMINAIRE.   Sees, France (Roman Catholic).   679
GRAND SEMINAIRE.   Sens, France (Roman Catholic).   680
GRAND SEMINAIRE.   42, Avenue de Paris - 02 -
   Soissons, France (Roman Catholic--Compagnie de
   Saint Sulpice) 1668.
   Library: 1668, 0, OB, OS, ___-20,000, F, F-S,
   50-___   681
FACULTES DOMINICAINES.   Le Saulchoir-Etoilles, 91
   Soissy-Sur-Seine, France (Roman Catholic--Domini-
   cans) 1905.
   Library: 1905, 5, OB, 400,000-250,000, F, own,
   SC, 500-500, Mi   682
COLLEGIUM WILHELMITANUM--SEMINAIRE PROTES-
   TANT.   1 bis, Quai Saint Thomas, Strasbourg 67
   (Bas-Rhin) France (Foundation St. Thomas--Strasbourg,
   Eglise de la Confession Augsbourg d'Alsace et de
   Lorraine, Eglise Reformee d'Alsace et de Lorraine)
   1544.
   Library: 1544, 1, OB, ___-60,000, F G, own,
   SC, 10-5   683
GRAND SEMINAIRE.   2, rue des Freres, Strasbourg
   (Bas-Rhin) France (Roman Catholic) 1683.   684
PALAIS UNIVERSITAIRE--FACULTE DE THEOLOGIE
   CATHOLIQUE.   Strasbourg (Bas-Rhin) 67, France
   (Roman Catholic--University of Strasbourg Catholic
   Faculty) 1903.
   Library: 1907, 1, OB, 18,665-18,665, F, own,
   F-S, 170-___   685
PALAIS UNIVERSITAIRE--INSTITUT D'HISTOIRE DU
   MOYEN AGE UNIVERSITE.   Strasbourg (Bas-Rhin)
   67, France (Roman Catholic) 1921.   686
GRAND SEMINAIRE.   Tarbes, France (Roman Catho-
   lic).   687
GRAND SEMINAIRE.   9, rue des Teintures, Toulouse,
   France (Roman Catholic).   688
INSTITUT CATHOLIQUE.   31, rue de la Fonderie, 31
   Toulouse, France (Roman Catholic) 1876.

France (cont.)
   Library: 1876, 2, OB,   -200,000, F, Old
   French Series, F-S, 150-80, Sl   689
GRAND SEMINAIRE. 8, rue Losserand, Tours 31,
   France (Roman Catholic) 1698.   690
GRAND SEMINAIRE. Rue de l'Isle, Troyes, France
   (Roman Catholic).   691
GRAND SEMINAIRE. Tulle, France (Roman Catholic). 692
GRAND SEMINAIRE. 75, rue Montplaisir, Valence,
   France (Roman Catholic).   693
GRAND SEMINAIRE. Vannes, France (Roman Catho-
   lic).   694
GRAND SEMINAIRE. Place de Mgr-Ginistry, Verdun
   (Meuse) France (Roman Catholic).   695
GRAND SEMINAIRE. 24, rue du Marechal Joffre, Ver-
   sailles, France (Roman Catholic).   696
GRAND SEMINAIRE DE NANCY. 54, Villers-les-Nancy,
   France, (Roman Catholic--Diocese de Nancy) 1805.
   Library: 1805, 1, OB, 100,000-80,000, F, 60-0   697
GRAND SEMINAIRE. Viviers, France (Roman Catho-
   lic).   698

Germany--Federal Republic of Germany
PHILOSOPHICAL-THEOLOGIE STUDIENAUSTALT DER
   SALESIANER. Benediktbeuren 8174, Germany
   (Roman Catholic).
   Bibliothek Don Boscos.   699
FREI UNIVERSITAT--SEMINAR FUR EVANGELISCHE-
   THEOLOGIE. Ihnestrasse 56, Berlin 33, Germany
   (Evangelische Kirche) 1957.   700
FREI UNIVERSITAT--SEMINAR FUR KATHOLISCHE
   THEOLOGIE. Ihnestrasse 31, Berlin 33, Germany
   (Roman Catholic).   701
HUMBOLDT-UNIVERSITAT--THEOLOGISCHER INSTITUT.
   10 Berlin, Marz-Engels-Platz, Dom Berlin, Germany
   (Evangelische Landeskirche Berlin-Brandenburg) 1810.
   Library: 1810, 0, 100,000-70,000, G, F-S, 35-35   702
KIRCHENGEMEINDE ALSTADT BIBLIOTHEK. Elsasser
   strasse 26, Bielefeld 4800, Germany, 1600.   703
UNIVERSITY OF BONN--OLD CATHOLIC FACULTY.
   The Reverend Professor Kuppers, Hauptegebaude
   11/120, Bonn 53, Germany (Old Catholic Church)
   1902.   704
RHEINISCHE FRIEDRICH-WILHELMS UNIVERSITATS--
   FACULTY OF CATHOLIC THEOLOGY. Lievfrauen-
   weg 3, Bonn, Germany (Roman Catholic) 1818.   705
RHEINISCHE FRIEDRICH-WILHELMS UNIVERSITATS--

FACULTY OF PROTESTANT THEOLOGY. An Hof
I-D, Bonn, Germany (Lutheran) 1777.   706
RUHR-UNIVERSITAT BOCHUM--ZENTRALES KATHO-
LIC THEOLOGIE SEMINAR. 463 Bochum-Querenburg,
Buscheystrasse, Postfach 2148, Germany (Roman
Catholic) 1965.
Library: 1965, 1, OB, OS, 75,000-20,000, F G I,
own, F-S, 140-140   707
SEMINAR DER ABTEILUNG FUR EVANGELISCHE
THEOLOGIE. 463 Bochum-Querenburg, Buschey-
strasse, Gebaude IA 1/40, Germany (Evangelical)
1963.
Library: 1963, 1, OS, 40,000-35,000, E G, A-Z,
F-S, 97-97, Sl Ma Mu   708
UNIVERSITAT BOCHUM. 4630 Bochum-Querenburg,
Im Lottental, Zeche Klosterbusch, Germany (Inde-
pendent) 1965.
Library: 1965, 6, OS, 450,000-80,000, G, own,
3,700-   709
PREDIGERSEMINAR DER BRAUNSCHWEIGSCHEN
EVANGELISCHE LUTHERAN LANDESKIRKEN.
Schutzenstrasse 22-33, Braunschweig 3300, Germany
(Lutheran) 1631.   710
ERZBISCHOFLICHE DIOZESAN-BIBLIOTHEK KOLN.
5 Kohn (Cologne), Gereonstrasse 2-4, Germany
(Roman Catholic--Erzbistum Koln) 1737.
Library: 1737, 8, OB, 135,000-125,000, G, Ac-
cession, SC 681-___, Sl Mu   711
DIOZESANPRIESTERSEMINAR. Dillingen-Donau 6/III,
Germany 8800 (Roman Catholic) 1549.   712
PREDIGERSEMINAR DER EVANGELISCHEN KIRCHEN
VON WESTFALEN. 1 Indenmannstrasse 68, Dort-
mund 4600, Germany, 1959.   713
BISCHOFLICHE-PHILOSOPHIE-THEOLOGISCHE HOCH-
SCHULE. 8833 Eichstatt/Bayern, Am Hofgarten 1,
Germany (Roman Catholic) 1564.
Bischofliche Seminarbibliothek Eichstatt: 19th cen-
tury, 3, OB, 350,000-150,000, G, Accession, SC,
10-10   714
CORVINUS-PREDIGERSEMINARS. Post Hunnerruck,
Ericksburg, Germany 3351 (Roman Catholic).   715
FRIEDRICH-ALEXANDER UNIVERSITATS--FACULTY
OF PROTESTANT THEOLOGY. Schlossplatz 4,
Erlangen, Germany (Lutheran) 1743.   716
SEMINAR FUR ALLGEMEINE KIRCHENGESCHICHTE.
Kochstrasse 6, Erlangen 8250, Germany, 1850.   717
SEMINAR FUR CHRISTLICHE OSTENS. Kochstrasse

Germany--Federal Republic of Germany (cont.)
6, Erlangen 8250, Germany, 1949.   718
SEMINAR FUR THEOLOGIE DES ALTES TESTAMENT.
Kochstrasse 6, Erlangen 8250, Germany.   719
METHODIST THEOLOGICAL SEMINARY.   6 Frankfurt/
m/strasse Ginnheimer, Landstrasse 180, Germany
(Methodist).   720
PHILOSOPHIE-THEOLOGIE HOCHSCHULE SANKT
GEORGE.   Offenbacher Landstrasse 224, Frankfurt-
Main, Sud 10, 6000, Germany (Roman Catholic)
1926.   721
CARITASBIBLIOTHEK.   78 Freiburg im Breisgau,
Werthmannplatz 4, Germany (Deutscher Caritasver-
band e. V.) 1896.
Library: 1896, 5, OS, 100,000-100,000, G, Acces-
sion, 650-   722
PHILOSOPHIE-THEOLOGIE HOCHSCHULE.   Domberg
38, Freising 8050, Germany (Roman Catholic) 1834. 723
PRIESTERSEMINAR.   Domberg 27, Freising 8050,
Germany (Roman Catholic).   724
PHILOSOPHIE-THEOLOGIE HOCHSCHULE.   Domplatz
5, Fulda 6400, Germany (Roman Catholic).   725
PREDIGERSEMINAR DER LANDESKIRCHE VON KIRC-
HESSEN-WULBERG.   Gesundbrunnen, Germany
(Protestant).   726
VEREINIGTE THEOLOGISCHE SEMINARE.   34 Gottin-
gen, Nikolausberger Weg 5b, Germany (Independent)
1878.
Library: 1878, 0, OB, OS, 60,000-35,000, own,
F-S   727
UNIVERSITAT HAMBURG--EVANGELISCH-THEOLO-
GISCHE FAKULTAT.   2 Hamburg 13, Von-Melle-
Park 6, Germany, 1954.
Library: 1954, 2, OB, OS, 50,000-50,000, G,
Subject, F-S 200-___, Ar Sl Pi Ma Mu   728
RUPRECHT-KARL-UNIVERSITATS--FACULTY OF THE-
OLOGY.   Alte Universitat, Schulgasse 4, Heidelberg,
Germany (Lutheran) 1386.   729
UNIVERSITAT HEIDELBERG--WISSENSCHAFTLICHE
THEOLOGISCHE SEMINAR.   6900 Heidelberg, Klinger-
teichstrasse 2 und Karlstrasse 4, F. 54/270 und 54/
271, Germany, 1895.
Library: 1895, 2, OS, 40,000-38,000, G, own, F-S,
759-759, Sl Mi Ma   730
ERZBISCHOFLICHES PRIESTERSEMINAR.   Beruhl,
Hildesheim, Germany (Roman Catholic).   731
CHRISTINA-ALBRECHTS-UNIVERSITATS--FACULTY

OF THEOLOGY. Neue Universitat, Olshausen-
strasse 40-60, Kiel, Germany (Protestant) 1665.   732
MISSIONSSEMINAR FREUDENBERG. 4180 Hau ub,
Kleve 4180, Germany.   733
PHILOSOPHIE-THEOLOGIE HOCHSCHULE UND
PRIESTERSEMINAR. Bischof Kaller Strasse 3,
Konigstern, Germany 6240 (Roman Catholic).   734
BISCHOFLICHES PRIESTERSEMINARS MAINZ.
Augustinerstrasse 34, Mainz 6500, Germany
(Roman Catholic) 1654.
Library: 1654, 4, OB, 150,000-145,000, G L,
Subject, F-S, 70-   735
JOHANNES GUTENBERG UNIVERSITATS--FACULTY
OF CATHOLIC THEOLOGY. Saarstrasse 21,
Mainz, Germany, 1477.   736
PHILIPPS UNIVERSITAT--THEOLOGISCHE FAKUL-
TAT. Lahntor, Marburg/Lahn., Germany
(Lutheran) 1527.   737
UNIVERSITAT MARBURG--THEOLOGISCHEN SEMI-
NARE. Marburg/Lahn., Lahntor 3, Germany,
1527.
Library: 1527, 1, OS, 80,000-40,000, G, own,
F-S, 150-150, Sl Ma   738
LUDWIG-MAXIMILIAN UNIVERSITATS--FACULTY OF
CATHOLIC THEOLOGY. Geschwister-Scholl-Platz
1, Munich, Germany (Roman Catholic) 1472.   739
BISCHOFLICHES PRIESTERSEMINAR. Uberwasser-
kirkplatz 8, Munster 4400, Germany (Roman Catho-
lic).   740
VEREINIGTE KATHOLIC THEOLOGIE SEMINARE DER
UNIVERSITAT. Johannisstrasse 8-10, Munster 4400,
Germany (Roman Catholic) 1773.   741
WESTFALLISCHEN-WILHELMS-UNIVERSITAT--SEMINARE
UND INSTITUTE DER EVANGELISCH-THEOLOGISCHEN
FAKULTAT. 4400 Munster, Universitatsstrasse 13-17,
Germany, 1780.
Library: 1914, 2, OS, 70,000-72,000, G, own, F-S,
SC, 135-135, Sl Mi Ma Mu   742
AUGUSTANA HOCHSCHULE. Neuendettelsau 8806, Ger-
many (Lutheran) 1947.   743
EVANGELISCHE LUTHERAN PREDIGERSEMINAR. Vech-
hofstrasse 24, Nurenberg 8600, Germany (Lutheran). 744
BISCHOFLICHES PRIESTERSEMINAR. Brosse Doms-
frieheit 5/6, Osnabruck 4500, Germany (Roman Cath-
olic).   745
ERZBISCHOFLICHE AKADEMISCHE--PAPSTLICHEN
FAKULTAT. 4790 Paderborn, Leostrasse 21,

Germany--Federal Republic of Germany (cont.)
Germany (Roman Catholic) 1614.
    Library: 1615, 7, OB, 250,000-160,005, G, Ac-
cession, SC, 330-___   746 •
PHILOSOPHIE-THEOLOGIE HOCHSCHULE. Michael-
gasse 13, Passau 8390, Germany (Roman Catholic)
1622.   747
EVANGELISCHE LUTHERAN PREDIGERSEMINAR.
Kieler Strasse 30, Preetz (Holstein) 2308, Germany
(Lutheran) 1896.   748
PHILOSOPHIE-THEOLOGIE HOCHSCHULE. Agidrenplatz
2, Regensburg 8400, Germany (Roman Catholic)
   1589..   749
MISSIONSPRIESTERSEMINAR. Siegburg/Rhineland,
Sankt Augustin 5205, Germany (Roman Catholic)
1924.   750
PRIESTERSEMINARS. 6720 Speyer Am Rhein, St.
Germansberg, Germany (Roman Catholic) 1826.
    Library: 1826, 0, OB, OS, 80,000-30,000, Sub-
ject, F-S, 95-___   751
PRIESTERSEMINARS TRIER. D-55 Trier, Jesuits-
strasse 13, Postfach 320, Germany (Bischofliches
Priesterseminar Trier) 1773.
    Bibliothek der Theologische Fakultat Trier: 1805,
7, OB, 200,000-125,000, G, Eppelsheim, SC, 357-
357, Sl Mi   752
KATHOLISCH-THEOLOGISCHES SEMINAR. 74 Tubin-
gen Liebermeisterstrasse 12, Germany (Roman
Catholic) 1817.
    Library: 1817, 4, OS, ___-60,000, G, own, F-S,
130-130, Sl   753
KIRCHLICHE HOCHSCHULE WUPPERTAL. Mission-
strasse 9, Wuppertal-Barmen, Germany (Lutheran).   754
UNIVERSITAT WURZBURG--THEOLOGISCHEN FAKUL-
TAT. 8700 Wurzburg, Sanderring 2, Germany
(Government) 1582.
    Library: 1803, 3, 70,000-70,000, E F G L, F-S,
SC, 250-250   755

Germany--German Democratic Republic
DIOZESANBIBLIOTHEK. 5100 Aachen, Mozartstrasse
7, Postfach 233, Germany (Bischofliche General-
vikariat 51, Aachen, Klosterplatz) 1938.
    Library: 1938, 2, OB, 150,000-90,066, G, 249-
249, Sl   756
DOMINICANEUM BIBLIOTEK. Eberburgweg 4, Aachen
5100, Germany (Roman Catholic) 1920.   757

ERZBISCHOFLICHES KLERIKALSEMINAR. Henricks-
damm 32, Bamberg, Germany (Roman Catholic).   758
KARMELITENBIBLIOTEK. Karmelitenplatz 1, Bam-
berg 8600, Germany (Roman Catholic).   759
KIRCHENBIBLIOTEK VON ST. NIKOLAI ZU SPANDAU.
Teltower Damm 118-122, Berlin 37, Germany (Roman
Catholic) 1532.   760
KIRCHLICHEN HOCHSCHULE BERLIN. Teltower Damm
118, Berlin 37, Germany (Evangelische Kirche Berlin-
Brandenburg) 1935.
Library: 1946, 0, 260,000-120,000, own, 300-   761
FREI UNIVERSITAT--RELIGIONSWISSENSCHAFTLICHES
INSTITUT. Boltzmannstrasse 4, Berlin 33, Ger-
many, 1948.   762
KIRCHLICHEN HOCHSCHULE. D 4813 Bethel, Fried-
hofsweg 67, Germany (Von Bodelschwinghsche An-
stalten/Bethel bei Bielefeld) 1905.
Library: 1905, 1, OB, 100,000-60,000, G, own,
F-S, 98-74   763
PHILOSOPHIE-THEOLOGIE STUDIEM. Domstrasse 10,
Erfurt, Germany (Roman Catholic).   764
BISCHOFLICHES PRIESTERSEMINAR. Ruhrtalstrasse
4-6, Essen 4300, Germany (Roman Catholic) 1958.   765
ERNST MORITZ ARNDT-UNIVERSITAT--INSTITUT FUR
THEOLOGIE. DDR-22 Greifswald, Domstrasse 11,
IV, Germany (Staatliche Institution, Evangelische
Kirche in Deutschland) 1456.
Library: 1880, 1, OS, 30,000-25,100, G, own, F-S,
66-50, Fi Sl   766
MARTIN LUTHER UNIVERSITAT--FACULTY OF THEOL-
OGY. Universitatplatz 8-9, Halle/Salle, Halle-Witten-
berg, Germany, 1506, 1694, 1933.   767
INSTITUT FUR THEOLOGIE UND ALLGEMEINE RE-
LIGIONSGESCHICTE. DDR X 69 Jena, Kahlaische
Strasse 7, Germany (Evangelisch-Lutherische
Fakultat der Friedrich-Schiller-Universitat) 1558.
Library: 1558, 1, OB, OS, 22,000-22,000, G,
own, F-S, 50-   768
INSTITUT FUR KIRCHENGESCHICHTE, INSTITUT
FUR NEUEN TESTAMENT, INSTITUT FUR PRAK-
TISCHE THEOLOGIE, INSTITUT FUR SYSTEMA-
TICISHE THEOLOGIE. Leipzig 701, Germany.
Library: 1945   769
KARL MARX UNIVERSITATS--FACULTY OF THEOLOGY.
Petersteinweg 8, Leipzig, Germany (Lutheran) 1409. 770
KARL MARX UNIVERSITATS--FACULTY OF THEOLOGY.
Ritterstrasse 14 C-1, Leipzig, Germany (Roman

Germany--German Democratic Republic (cont.)
    Catholic) 1409.   771
LUTHERISCHEN THEOLOGISCHEN HOCHSCHULE. 637
    Oberusel/Js. , Altkonigstrasse 50, Germany (Ev. -
    Luth. (altluth) Kirche und Ev. -Luth. Freikirche)
    1947.
    Library: 1947, 0, OB, OS, 15,000-14,000, A-Z,
    F-S   772
UNIVERSITAT ROSTOCK--THEOLOGISCHE FAKULTAT.
    Stalinplatz, Rostock, Germany (Lutheran) 1419.   773
BISCHOFLICHES PRIESTERSEMINAR. Rottenburg,
    Germany (Roman Catholic).   774

Greece
ALTHINISSIN ETHNIKON KAI KAPODISTRIAKON
    PANEPISITIMION--FACULTY OF THEOLOGY. Odos
    Panepisitimion, Athens, Greece, 1837.   775
UNIVERSITE DE SALONIQUE--FACULTE DE THE-
    OLOGIE. Salonika, Greece (Eastern Orthodox)
    1925.   776
RIZERIOS ECCLESIASTIKI SCHOLI LECFOROS
    BASILISIS SOPHIAS. Sofias, Greece.   777
ARISTOTELIAN PANEPISITIMION FACULTY OF THE-
    OLOGY. Thessaloniki, Greece, 1925.   778
TREIS LERARHOI BIBLIOTHEKA. Odoa Demetriados,
    Volos, Greece, 1907.   779

Hungary
BAPTIST THEOLOGICAL SEMINARY. Budapest,
    Hungary (Baptist).   780
CENTRAL CATHOLIC SEMINARY. Budapest, Hungary
    (Roman Catholic) 1775.   781
JEWISH THEOLOGICAL SEMINARY OF HUNGARY.
    VIII. , Jozsef-Korut 27, Budapest, Hungary (Jewish)
    1877.
    Library: 1877, 4, OB, 100,000-60,000, SC,
    30-   782
ORSZAGOS EVANGELIKUS KONYVTAR (LIBRARY OF
    THE EVANGELICAL LUTHERAN CHURCH IN HUN-
    GARY). Budapest, VIII. , Ulloi ut 24, Hungary
    (Evangelikus Orszagos Egyhaz) 1923.
    Library: 1923, 3, 110,000, E Greek Hebrew, Sub-
    ject, F-S, SC, 81-   783
REFORMED ACADEMY OF THEOLOGY. IX. Raday-
    utca 28. sz. , Budapest, Hungary (Reformed Church
    of Hungary) 1855.
    Collection Raday: 1711, 4, OB, OS, 125,000-

125,000, own, Hungarian, SC, 120-___, Ar   784
DEBRECENI REFORMATUS THEOLOGIAI SEMINARY.
Kalvin Ter 16, Debrecen, Hungary (Reformed) 1914.   785
LIBRARY OF THE ESZTERGON CATHEDRAL.   Baycsy-
Zsilinszky-U, Esztergon, Hungary.   786
LIBRARY OF THE REFORMED CHURCH.   Saros-
patale, Radoczy U-1, Hungary (Reformed Church).   787

Iceland
UNIVERSITY OF ICELAND--FACULTY OF THEOLOGY.
Reykjavik, Iceland (Protestant) 1911.   788

Ireland
ST. PATRICK'S COLLEGE.   Carlow, Ireland (Roman
Catholic).   789
ALL HALLOWS COLLEGE.   Drumcondra, Dublin, Ire-
land (Roman Catholic).   790
DUBLINENSE COLLEGIUM MAXIMUM ST. JOSEPH.
Milltown Park, Ballsbridge, Dublin, Ireland (Roman
Catholic--Society of Jesus) 1889.   791
HOLY CROSS COLLEGE.   Clonliffe Road, Dublin 3,
Ireland, 1859.
Library: 1859, 1, OB, OS, 20,000-20,000, E L,
F-S, 20-10   792
UNIVERSITY OF DUBLIN--TRINITY COLLEGE.   Dublin,
Ireland, 1591.
Library: 1732, 0, OB, OS, 2,000,000-1,000,000,
E, DDC and Shelf, SC, 5,000-2,000, Ma Mu   793
ST. KIERAN'S COLLEGE.   Kilkenny, Ireland (Roman
Catholic).   794
ST. PATRICK'S COLLEGE.   Maynooth, County Kildare,
Ireland (Roman Catholic) 1795.
Library: 1800, 1, OB, OS, 60,000-60,000, E F G
L S, Sorbonne Uppsala Cutter, F-S, SC, 240-___,
Sl Pi Ma Mu   795
ST. PATRICK'S COLLEGE.   Thurles, Ireland (Roman
Catholic).   796
ST. JOHN'S COLLEGE.   Waterford, Ireland (Roman
Catholic).   797
ST. PETER'S COLLEGE.   Wexford, Ireland (Roman
Catholic).   798

Ireland, North
EDGEHILL THEOLOGICAL COLLEGE.   Lennoxvale,
Belfast, North Ireland (Methodist) 1926.   799
HANDSWORTH METHODIST COLLEGE. Lennoxvale,
Belfast, North Ireland (Methodist).   800

Ireland, North (cont.)
PRESBYTERIAN COLLEGE.   Botanic Avenue, Belfast
7, North Ireland (Presbyterian Church in Ireland)
1853.
Library: 1853, 2, OS, 30,000-30,000, E, DDC,
SC, 40-0   801
ST. MALACHY'S COLLEGE.   Belfast, North Ireland
(Roman Catholic).   802

Italy
SEMINARIO MAGGIORE.   Via S. Marino 4, Acireale
(Catania) Italy (Roman Catholic).   803
SEMINARIO MAGGIORE.   Piazza Duomo, Acqui (Ales-
sandria) Italy (Roman Catholic).   804
SEMINARIO MAGGIORE.   Piazza Don Minzoni, Agri-
gento, Italy (Roman Catholic).   805
SEMINARIO MAGGIORE.   Alba, Italy (Roman Catholic). 806
SEMINARIO DEL VESCOVILE.   Lungomare A, D, Ira,
Albenga (Savona) Italy (Roman Catholic).   807
SEMINARIO VESCOVILE.   Via Vochiere 14, Alessandria
(Piemontre) Italy (Roman Catholic).   808
PONTIFICIO COLLEGIO LEONIANO.   Anagni, Italy
(Roman Catholic).   809
SEMINARIO MAGGIORE.   Aosta, Italy (Roman Catholic)
1772.
Library: 1933, 1, OB, OS, 25,000-25,000, F I,
International, SC, 3-___, Fi Mu   ·   810
SEMINARIO MAGGIORE.   Arezzo, Italy (Roman Catho-
lic).   811
SEMINARIO MAGGIORE.   Largo L Cattaneo, Ascoli
Piceno, Italy (Roman Catholic).   812
PONTIFICIO SEMINARIO REGIONALE UMBRO PIO
XI.   Assisi, (Perugia) Italy (Roman Catholic).   813
SEMINARIO VESCOVILE.   Piazza sel Seminario, Asti,
Italy (Roman Catholic).   814
SEMINARIO VESCOVILE.   Piazza S. Agostinio, Bag-
noregio (Viterbo) Italy (Roman Catholic).   815
GREGORIANO SEMINARIO.   Belluno (Trentino) Italy
(Roman Catholic).   816
PONTIFICIO SEMINARIO REGIONALE PIO X.   Via
degli Atlantici 55, Benevento, Italy (Roman Catho-
lic).   817
SEMINARIO MAGGIORE.   Via Arena, Bergamo, Italy
(Roman Catholic).   818
SEMINARIO MAGGIORE.   Via Seminario 9, Bielle,
Italy (Roman Catholic).   819
SEMINARIO MAGGIORE.   Bobbio, Italy (Roman

Catholic). 820
PONTIFICIO SEMINARIO REGIONALE. Via di Bam-
bino, Bologna (Emilia) Italy (Roman Catholic) 1919. 821
SEMINARIO MAGGIORE. Bordighera, Italy (Roman
Catholic). 822
SEMINARIO VESCOVILE "SANTANGELO." Via Gezio
Calani 30, Brescia, Italy (Roman Catholic). 823
PRIESTERSEMINARS BRIXEN-BRESSANONE. Brixen-
Bressanone (BZ), Italy (Roman Catholic) 1609.
Library: 1609, 2, OB, OS, 70,000-70,000, G L,
Staats Bibliotek Munich, SC, 40-5, Ar Mi Ma 824
SEMINARIO MAGGIORE. Piazza S. Francesco 9,
Caltagirone, Italy (Roman Catholic). 825
SEMINARIO VESCOVILE. Via Regina Margharetta 51,
Caltanissetta (Sicily) Italy (Roman Catholic). 826
SEMINARIO MAGGIORE. Via Bongiovanni 9, Camerino,
Italy (Roman Catholic). 827
SEMINARIO MAGGIORE "SAN GIOVANNI BATISTA."
Corso Fanti 44, Carpi, Italy (Roman Catholic). 828
SEMINARIO MAGGIORE. Piazza Nazari di Calabriana,
Casale Monferrato, Italy (Roman Catholic). 829
SEMINARIO MAGGIORE "S. AGATA." Viale Oderico
da Prodenone, Catania, Italy (Roman Catholic). 830
PONTIFICIO SEMINARIO REGIONALE S. PIO X. Viale
S. Pio X, Catanzaro, Italy (Roman Catholic). 831
SEMINARIO MAGGIORE. Piazza Duomo, Cefalu
(Palermo) Italy (Roman Catholic). 832
SEMINARIO VESCOVILE. Piazza Nostra Signore
dell'Orto, Chiavari (Grovna) Italy (Roman Catholic). 833
COLLEGIO MASSINO SOCIETY JESUS. Casa S. An-
tonio, Chieri (Torino) Italy (Roman Catholic--
Society of Jesus) 1890. 834
PONTIFICIO SEMINARIO REGIONALE CURIA AR-
CIVESCOVILE. Via Arcivescovada 21, Chieti
(Abruzzi) Italy (Roman Catholic). 835
SEMINARIO VESCOVILE. Chioggia (Venezia) Italy
(Roman Catholic).
Library: 1, OB, ___-10,000, I L, 20-___ 836
SEMINARIO MAGGIORE -- COMO. Viale C. Battisti,
8, Como, Italy (Roman Catholic) 1818.
Library: 1818, 2, OB, 50,000-9,000, I L, Authors,
SC, Ar Sl 837
SEMINARIO CONVITTO VESCOVILE. Via Morgan-
tini 1, Conversano (Bari) Italy (Roman Catholic). 838
SEMINARIO MAGGIORE. Via Vaguatti 4, Cortina,
Italy (Roman Catholic). 839
BIBLIOTECA SEMINARIO. Dante Alighieri Street 24,

Italy (cont.)
   Crema (CR) Italy. (Date of seminary: 1935).
   Library: 1910, 3, OB, OS, 25,000-15,000 I, A-
   Z, SC, 30-___, Ar Fi Sl Pi Ma Mu   840
SEMINARIO VESCOVILE.   Via Milano 5, Cremona,
   Italy (Roman Catholic) 1592.   841
PONTIFICIO SEMINARIO REGIONALE.   Sardo del S.
   Cuore di Gesu, Cuglieri, Italy (Roman Catholic).   842
SEMINARIO MAGGIORE.   Via Amedeo Rossi 28,
   Cuneo, Italy (Roman Catholic).   843
SEMINARIO MAGGIORE DELLA DIOCESI DE FAENZA.
   Stradone 30, Faenza, Italy (Roman Catholic) 1576.
   Biblioteca Cardinal Gaetano Creognani: 1948, 2,
   OB, OS, 70,000-55,000, F I, International Card
   Catalog, SC, 40-0, Ar Sl   844
PONTIFICIO SEMINARIO REGIONALE MARCHIGIANO
   PIO XI.   Via Flaminia, Fano, Italy (Roman Catho-
   lic).   845
SEMINARIO VESCOVILE DI FELTRE.   Feltre (Bel-
   luno) Italy (Roman Catholic) 1688.   846
SEMINARIO MAGGIORE.   Corso Cefalonia 4, Fermo,
   Italy (Roman Catholic).   847
SEMINARIO MAGGIORE DELL'ASSUNZIONE.   G. Fab-
   bri 178, Ferrara, Italy (Roman Catholic) 1717.   848
SEMINARIO MAGGIORE.   Fidenza, Italy (Roman
   Catholic).   849
SEMINARIO MAGGIORE.   Piazza Mino 15, Fiesole,
   Italy (Roman Catholic).   850
SEMINARIO MAGGIORE.   Lungarno Soderini 19,
   Florence, Italy (Roman Catholic).   851
SEMINARIO MAGGIORE.   Via Guiseppi Milano, Fossano,
   Italy (Roman Catholic).   852
SEMINARIO MAGGIORE.   Via Porta d'Archi 14, Genoa,
   Italy (Roman Catholic).   853
SEMINARIO ARCIVESCOVILE.   Via B Alvcano 18,
   Gorizia, Italy (Roman Catholic).   854
SEMINARIO MAGGIORE.   Via Francesco Ferrucci 11,
   Grosseto, Italy (Roman Catholic).   855
SEMINARIO MAGGIORE.   Piazza Vittorio Veneto 3,
   Guastalla, Italy (Roman Catholic).   856
SEMINARIO MAGGIORE.   Via Garibaldi 9, Imola
   (Bologna) Italy (Roman Catholic).   857
SEMINARIO MAGGIORE.   Via S. Varmondo, Ivres
   (Torino) Italy (Roman Catholic).   858
SEMINARIO VESCOVILE.   Lecce, Italy (Roman Catho-
   lic).
   Biblioteca Innocenziana.   859

SEMINARIO MAGGIORE. Via XX Settembre 30, Lodi,
Italy (Roman Catholic). 860
SEMINARIO MAGGIORE. Borgo Giannotti-Vallebuia,
Lucca, Italy (Roman Catholic). 861
SEMINARIO MAGGIORE. Contrada S. Lucia, Macerata,
Italy (Roman Catholic). 862
SEMINARIO VESCOVILE. Piazza della Republica 1814,
Mazara del Vallo, Italy (Roman Catholic) 1814. 863
SEMINARIO MAGGIORE. Messina, Italy (Roman Catho-
lic). 864
SEMINARIO METROPOLITANO. Corso Canal Chiaro
149, Modena, Italy (Roman Catholic). 865
PONTIFICIO SEMINARIO REGIONALE APPULO PIO XI.
Viale Pio XI, Molfetta (Gari) Italy (Roman Catho-
lic). 866
SEMINARIO MAGGIORE. Via del Seminario 8, Mondovi
(Cuneo) Italy (Roman Catholic). 867
TORRES SEMINARIO ARCIVESCOVILE. Via Arcivesco-
vado 1, Monreale, Italy (Roman Catholic). 868
SEMINARIO MAGGIORE. Via Cairoli 20, Montova,
Italy (Roman Catholic). 869
SEMINARIO MAGGIORE ARCIVESCOVILE--FACOLTA
TEOLOGICA PER L'AICHI DIOCESI NAPOLETANA.
Naples, Italy (Roman Catholic) 1941. 870
PONTIFICIA FACOLTA TEOLOGICA "S. LUIGI."
Via Petrarca, 115, Naples, Italy (Roman Catholic--
Society of Jesus) 1898.
Library: 1898, 3, OB, 120,000-45,000, I L, SC,
250-___, Ma 871
SEMINARIO ARCIVESCOVILE. Viale Aminei-Capodi-
monte, Naples, Italy (Roman Catholic) 1851. 872
SEMINARIO MAGGIORE. Largo S. Biaggio, Nicosia,
Italy (Roman Catholic). 873
SEMINARIO MAGGIORE. Via Gioberti, Noto (Siracusa)
Italy (Roman Catholic). 874
SEMINARIO VESCOVILE DI NOVARA. Via Monte San
Gabriele 60, Novara, Italy (Roman Catholic) 1650.
Library: 1650, 1, OB, 100,000-70,000, I, Size,
F-S, SC, 50- 875
SEMINARIO MAGGIORE. Via del Seminario 11, Padova,
Italy (Roman Catholic). 876
SEMINARIO MAGGIORE. Via dell'Inoronazione, Pa-
lermo, Italy (Roman Catholic). 877
SEMINARIO MAGGIORE. Via Cardinal Ferrari 1,
Parma, Italy (Roman Catholic). 878
SEMINARIO MAGGIORE. Via Menocchio 26, Pavia,
Italy (Roman Catholic). 879

Italy (cont.)
COLLEGIO ALBERONI. Via Emilia Parmense 77,
Piacenza, Italy (Collegio Alberoni direct for Vincen-
tians Fathers) 1751.
  Biblioteca Cardinale Giulio Alberoni: 1751, 2, OS,
  100,000-69,000, I L, Authors, SC, 236-___, Ar
  Pi Ma Mu   880
SEMINARIO MAGGIORE. Via Scalabrini 67, Piacenza,
Italy (Roman Catholic).   881
SEMINARIO MAGGIORE. Via La Bella 3, Piazza Ar-
merins, Italy (Roman Catholic).   882
SEMINARIO MAGGIORE. Via Trieste 22, Pinerolo
(Torino) Italy (Roman Catholic).   883
SEMINARIO ARCIVESCOVILE S. CATERINA. Piazza
S. Caterina 4, Pisa, Italy (Roman Catholic) 1759.
  Biblioteca Cateriniana: 1759, 2, OB, OS, 55,000-
  35,000, I L, International, SC, 50-___, Ar   884
SEMINARIO MAGGIORE. Via Puccini 18, Pistoia,
Italy (Roman Catholic).   885
SEMINARIO MAGGIORE. Piazza S. Francesco, Pontre-
moli, Italy (Roman Catholic).   886
SEMINARIO MAGGIORE. Pordenone, Italy (Roman
Catholic).   887
SEMINARIO MAGGIORE. Piazza Duomo 4, Ravenna,
Italy (Roman Catholic).   888
PONTIFICIO SEMINARIO REGIONALE CALABRO PIO
XI. Viale Pio XI, Reggio di Calabria 236, Italy
(Roman Catholic) 1933.   889
SEMINARIO URBANO. Viale Timavo 93, Reggio nell'
Emilia, Italy (Roman Catholic) 1820.   890
SEMINARIO DIOCESANO. Via Vasari 30, Rimini (Fo)
Italy (Roman Catholic--Sacerdoti Diocesani) 1600.
  Library: 1700, 2, 30,000-10,000, F I, 81-___, Ar   891
SEMINARIO MAGGIORE. Rivoli, Italy (Roman Catho-
lic).   892
ACADEMIA PONTIFICIA ECCLESIASTICA. Vatican
City, Rome, Italy (Roman Catholic) 1701.   893
COLLEGIO INTERNAZIONALE DEI CARMELITANI--
FACOLTA TEOLOGICA. Scalzi, Vatican City,
Rome, Italy (Roman Catholic) 1701.   894
FACOLTA TEOLOGICA MARIANUM. Viale Trenta
Aprile n. 6, Rome 856, Italy (Roman Catholic--
Ordine dei Servi di Maria) 1666.
  Library: 1666, 3, OS, 200,000-80,000, F I L,
  CDU, SC, 400-___, Fi Sl Ma   895
FACOLTAS TEOLOGICAS SS. THERESIAE A JESU ET
JOANNIS A CRUCE. Piazza S. Pancrazio 5A, Vati-

can City, Rome, Italy (Roman Catholic) 1926.   896
INSTITUTO INTERNAZIONALE REGINA MUNDI. Via
Crescenzio 86, Vatican City, Rome, Italy (Roman
Catholic) 1940.   897
PONTIFICIA ATENEO DI S. ANSELMO. Via Porta
Lavernale 19, Vatican City, Rome, Italy (Roman
Catholic) 1687.   898
PONTIFICIA FACOLTA TEOLOGICA S. BONAVENTURA.
Via S. Teodoro 42, Vatican City, Rome, Italy
(Roman Catholic) 1905.   899
PONTIFICIA UNIVERSITA GREGORIANA. Piazza della
Pilotta 4, Vatican City, Rome, Italy (Roman Catholic)
1554.   900
PONTIFICIA UNIVERSITA LATERANENSE. Piazza S.
Giovanni in Laterano, Rome 4, Italy (Roman Catholic--
Holy See) 1773.
Biblioteca Generale "Pio IX": 1773, 3, OS,
-250,000, own, L, F-S, SC, 426-421   901
PONTIFICIA UNIVERSITA URBANIANA DE PROPA-
GANDA FIDES. Via Urbana VIII, 16, Vatican City,
Rome, Italy (Roman Catholic) 1648.   902
PONTIFICII ATHENAEI ANTONIANI. Via Merulana,
124/B, Rome 401, Italy (Roman Catholic--Ordo
Fratrum Minorum) 1890.
Library: 1890, 7, OB, 500,000-193,134, Vatican,
SC, 2,505-___, SI   903
PONTIFICIO INSTITUTIO BIBLICO. Piazza Pilotta 25,
Vatican City, Rome, Italy (Roman Catholic) 1909.   904
PONTIFICIO INSTITUTIO DE MUSICA SACRA. Piazza
S. Agostino 20a, Vatican City, Rome, Italy (Roman
Catholic) 1911.   905
PONTIFICUM ATHENAEUM INTERNATIONALE "ANGELI-
CUM." Salito del Griollo 1, Vatican City, Rome,
Italy (Roman Catholic) 1577.   906
PONTIFICUM ATHENAEUM SALESIANUM. Via Marsala
42, Vatican City, Rome, Italy (Roman Catholic)
1940.   907
PONTIFICUM INSTITUTIENTUM ORIENTALIUM
STUDIORIUM. Piazza Santa Maria Maggiore, Vati-
can City, Rome, Italy (Roman Catholic) 1917.   908
UNIVERSITA S. TOMMASO. Largo Angelicum 1,
Rome, Italy (Roman Catholic--Dominican Fathers--
Ordo Fratrum Praedicatorum) 1577.
Library: 1577, 3, OB, 300,000-150,000, L, LC
and Petersen, F-S, 320-200   909
SEMINARIO VESCOVILE. Via G Sichirollo 23, Rovigo,
Italy (Roman Catholic).   910

Italy (cont.)
SEMINARIO MAGGIORE.   S. Muniato (Pisa) Italy
   (Roman Catholic) 1830.   911
PONTIFICIO SEMINARIO REGIONALE SALERNITANO--
   LUCANO PIO XI.   1 Via Pio XI, Salerno, Italy
   (Roman Catholic).   912
SEMINARIO MAGGIORE COLLEGIO DI S. BERNARDINO.
   Via S. Nicola 26, Saluzzo, Italy (Roman Catholic).   913
SEMINARIO MAGGIORE.   Sarzana, Italy (Roman
   Catholic).   914
SEMINARIO MAGGIORE.   Via Leopoldo Ponzone 5,
   Savona, Italy (Roman Catholic).   915
SEMINARIO VESCOVILE.   Via Scapezzano 1 bis, Seni-
   gallia (Ancona) Italy (Roman Catholic).   916
PONTIFICIO SEMINARIO REGIONALE PIO XII.   Piazza
   S. Francesco, Siena, Italy (Roman Catholic).   917
SEMINARIO MAGGIORE.   Piazza Duomo 5, Syracuse,
   Italy (Roman Catholic).   918
PONTIFICIO ATENEO SALESIANO.   Via Sebastiano
   Caboto 27, Piazza Conti Rebaudengo 22, Turin, Italy
   (Roman Catholic) 1936.   919
SEMINARIO MAGGIORE.   Piazza S. Guisto 7, Susa
   (Torino) Italy (Roman Catholic).   920
SEMINARIO MAGGIORE.   Via del Seminario, Tortona,
   Italy (Roman Catholic).   921
SEMINARIO ARCIVESCOVILE MINOR.   Via 3 Novembre
   8, Trento, Italy (Roman Catholic).   922
SEMINARIO MAGGIORE.   Piazza S. Benedetto XI, Tre-
   viso, Italy (Roman Catholic).   923
SEMINARIO VESCOVILE DI TRIESTE.   Via Besenghi
   16, Trieste, Italy (Roman Catholic) 1960.
   Library: 1960, 2, OB, OS, 25,000-22,300, F I,
   Size, SC, 172-__, Ar Mu VF   924
SEMINARIO MAGGIORE.   Viale Ungheria 2, Udine,
   Italy (Roman Catholic).   925
SEMINARIO ARCIVESCOVILE--PONTIFICIA FACOLTA
   TEOLOGICA DE MILANO.   Venegone Inferiore,
   Italy (Roman Catholic) 1580.   926
SEMINARIO PATRIARCALE.   Dorsouro 1, Venice,
   Italy (Roman Catholic).   927
SEMINARIO MAGGIORE.   Piazza S. Eusebio, Vercelli,
   Italy (Roman Catholic).   928
SEMINARIO MAGGIORE.   Via del Seminario 8, Verona,
   Italy (Roman Catholic).   929
SEMINARIO MAGGIORE.   Borgo S. Lucia, Vicenza,
   Italy (Roman Catholic).   930
SEMINARIO MAGGIORE.   Vicolo del Seminario 5,

Vigevano (Pavia) Italy (Roman Catholic). 931
PONTIFICIO SEMINARIO REGIONALE PIO XI. La
Quercia, Viterbo, Italy (Roman Catholic). 932
LARGO SEMINARIO. Vittorio Veneto, Italy (Roman
Catholic). 933

Luxembourg

GRAND SEMINAIRE. Mont St. Lambert, Luxembourg
(Roman Catholic). 934

Malta

ARCHDIOCESAN SEMINARY OF THE ASSUMPTION OF
THE B.V.M. Floriana, Malta (Roman Catholic). 935
ROYAL UNIVERSITY OF MALTA. St. Paul Street,
Valletta, Malta (Roman Catholic--Society of Jesus)
1769.
Library: 1592 936
EPISCOPAL SEMINARY. Victoria, Malta (Roman
Catholic). 937

Netherlands

OUD-KATHOLIEK SEMINARIE. Koningin Wilhelmina-
laan 5, Amersfoort, Netherlands (Oud-Katholieke
Kerk van Nederland) 1725.
Library: 1726, 1, OB, ___-10,000, F L, Cards,
SC, 20-20 938
DOOPSGEZINDE GEMEENTE. Singel 452, Amsterdam
(C), Netherlands (Algemene Doopsgezinde Societeit,
Doopsgezinde Gemeente Amsterdam, Mennonite
Church) 1811.
Bibliotheek en Archiefkamer: 1680, 1, OB, 50,000-
50,000+, D, own, SC, 25-25, Ar 939
ETS HAIN. Rapenburger Street 197, Amsterdam,
Netherlands (Portuguese Israelitish Community of
Amsterdam) 1637.
Library: 1637, 1, OB, 25,000-25,000, Hebrew,
F-S, SC, 10-0, Mu 940
THEOLOGISCHE HOGESCHOOL. Keizersgracht 105,
Amsterdam, Netherlands (Roman Catholic--Society
of Jesus) 1852.
Library: 1852, 6, OB, ___-300,000, SC, 600-0,
Mi 941
FREE UNIVERSITY. De Boelelaan 1115, Amsterdam-
Buitenveldert, Netherlands (The Churches of the
Reformation in the Netherlands) 1880.
Library: 1880, 56, OB, 200,000-100,000, D E F G,
own, SC, 500-450 942

Netherlands (cont.)
FREE UNIVERSITY OF AMSTERDAM--THEOLOGICAL
   FACULTY. Keizersgracht 164, Amsterdam,
   Netherlands (Lutheran) 1632.   943
UNIVERSITET VAN AMSTERDAM--FACULTY OF THE-
   OLOGY. Spui 21, Amsterdam, Netherlands (Inde-
   pendent) 1632.   944
SEMINARIE BIBLIOTHEEK. Airih Weg 348, Apel-
   doorn, Netherlands (Roman Catholic) 1818.   945
GROOT SEMINARIE. Liesbosloan 315, Breda, Nether-
   lands (Roman Catholic) 1911.   946
GROOT SEMINARIE "RIJSENBERG." Driebergen,
   Netherlands (Roman Catholic).   947
THEOLOGISCH INSTITUUT RYVSUNIVERSITEIT
   GRONINGEN. Oude Kyv. in 't Jatstraat g, Gronin-
   gen, Netherlands (Independent) 1947.
   Library: 1947, OS, 5,400-3,700, D E F G, own,
   70-0, Ar Sl Mi Pi Ma Mu   948
GROOT SEMINARIE. Ryksweg 9, Haaren (N. B.)
   Netherlands (Roman Catholic--Diocese of 's-Her-
   togenbosch) 1498.
   Library: 1498, 1, OB, 120,000-100,000, D E F
   G L, Size, SC, 100-40, Ar Ma   949
SEMINARIE ST. GABRIEL. Provinciale weg Oost 62,
   Haastrecht, Netherlands (Roman Catholic).   950
COLLEGE HAGEVELD. Cruguiusweg 15, Heemstede,
   Netherlands (Roman Catholic--Diocese of Haarlem--
   Secular Priests) 1817.
   Library: 1817, 1, OB, 30,000-20,000 D L, Sub-
   ject and Location, F-S, SC, 15-___, Ar Pi Ma Mu   951
GROOT SEMINARIE. Hoeven, Netherlands (Roman
   Catholic).   952
RIJKSUNIVERSITEIT TE LEIDEN--FACULTY OF THE-
   OLOGY. Stationweg 46, Leiden, Netherlands (Inde-
   pendent) 1575.   953
BIBLIOTHEEK CANISIANUM. Tongersestraat 53,
   Maastricht, Netherlands (Roman Catholic--Society
   of Jesus) 1852.
   Library: 1852, 10, OB, 300,000-250,000, own,
   SC, 500-___, Ar Fi Sl Mi Pi Ma Mu VF   954
"BERCHMANIANUM" PHILOSOPHISCHE FACULTEIT
   S. T. Nijmgen, Netherlands (Roman Catholic--So-
   ciety of Jesus) 1934.   955
KATHOLIEKE UNIVERSITIET TE NJIMGEN--FACULTY
   OF THEOLOGY. Annastraat 333, Njimgen, Nether-
   lands (Roman Catholic) 1923.   956
ZEUDING DER NEDERLANDS HERVORNDE KERK.

Leidse Straatweg 11, Oegstgeest, Netherlands.   957
MONTFORTAANS GROOT SEMINARIE. Montforlan
12, Oirschot, Netherlands (Roman Catholic) 1903.   958
GROOT SEMINARIE. Swalmerstraat, Roermond,
Netherlands (Roman Catholic).   959
RIJKSUNIVERSITEIT TE UTRECHT--FACULTY OF
THEOLOGY. Kromme Weinwegracht 29, Utrecht,
Netherlands (Independent) 1636.   960
BISCHOPPELYK GROOT SEMINARIE MGR. AEGNEVENT-
LOAN. Warmond, Netherlands (Roman Catholic)
1779.   961
MORAVIAN THEOLOGICAL SEMINARY. Lageweg 4-5,
Zeist, Netherlands (Moravian Church of the Nether-
lands) 1902.   962

Norway
FREE FACULTY OF NORWAY. St. Olavsgt. 29, Oslo
I, Norway (Lutheran) 1904.
Menighetsfakultetets Bibliotek: 1904, 1, OS, ___-
7,100, E G Norwegian, F-S, 65-40   963
UNIVERSITET I OSLO--FACULTY OF THEOLOGY.
Karl Johanasgate 47, Oslo Norway (Independent)
1811.   964

Poland
SEMINARIUM DUCHOWNE. ul. Stominskiego 8,
Bialystok, Poland (Roman Catholic).   965
SEMINARIUM DUCHOWNE. Drohiczyn, Poland (Roman
Catholic).   966
SEMINARIUM DUCHOWNE. Gdansk, Poland (Roman
Catholic).   967
SEMINARIUM DUCHOWNE. ul. Seminariyjna 2, Gneiz-
no, Poland (Roman Catholic).   968
SEMINARIUM DUCHOWNE. ul. Warscawska 36, Gor-
zoro, Poland (Roman Catholic).   969
SEMINARIUM DUCHOWNE. ul. Swierzcewskiego 27,
Kielce, Poland (Roman Catholic).   970
SEMINARIUM DUCHOWNE. ul. Bernardynska 3, Kra-
kow, Poland (Roman Catholic).   971
SEMINARIUM DUCHOWNE KRAKOWSKIE. Krakow,
Poland (Roman Catholic).   972
SEMINARIUM DUCHOWNE SLASKIE. Krakow, Poland
(Roman Catholic).   973
SEMINARIUM DUCHOWNE. ul. Worcella, Lodz, Poland
(Roman Catholic).   974
SEMINARIUM DUCHOWNE. ul. 22 Lipca 4, Lomza,
Poland (Roman Catholic).   975

Poland (cont.)
SEMINARIUM DUCHOWNE.   Lubaczow, Poland (Roman
    Catholic).   976
KATOLICK UNIVERSYTET LUBELSKI--FACULTY OF
    THEOLOGY.   Aleje Raclawickie 14, Lublin, Poland
    (Roman Catholic) 1918.   977
SEMINARIUM DUCHOWNE.   ul. Buczka 8, Lublin,
    Poland (Roman Catholic).   978
SEMINARIUM DUCHOWNE.   ul. Marianska 3, Olsztyn,
    Poland (Roman Catholic).   979
SEMINARIUM DUCHOWNE.   Opole, Poland (Roman
    Catholic).   980
SEMINARIUM DUCHOWNE.   Pl. Mariacki 7, Pelplin,
    Poland (Roman Catholic).   981
SEMINARIUM DUCHOWNE.   Plock, Poland (Roman
    Catholic).   982
SEMINARIUM DUCHOWNE.   ul. Wiezowa 2-4, Poznan,
    Poland (Roman Catholic).   983
SEMINARIUM DUCHOWNE.   ul. Lekawskiego 1,
    Przemyse, Poland (Roman Catholic).   984
SEMINARIUM DUCHOWNE.   Sandomierz, Poland
    (Roman Catholic).   985
SEMINARIUM DUCHOWNE.   ul. 1 Maja 42, Siedlce,
    Poland (Roman Catholic).   986
SEMINARIUM DUCHOWNE.   ul. J. Hrasickiego 6,
    Tarnow, Poland (Roman Catholic).   987
ACADEMY OF THEOLOGY.   ul. Duga 43, Warsaw,
    Poland (Lutheran, Old Catholic, Reformed).   988
PRAVOSLAWNA CHRESCIJAUSKII AKADEMII TEOLO-
    GICSNOJ.   ul. Paryska 27, Sekcija, Warsaw 33,
    Poland (Eastern Orthodox).   989
SEMINARIUM DUCHOWNE.   Krakowski Przedemiescie
    52/54, Warsaw, Poland (Roman Catholic).   990
SEMINARIUM DUCHOWNE.   ul. Seminaryiska 3,
    Wloclawek, Poland (Roman Catholic).   991
SEMINARIUM DUCHOWNE.   Pl. Katedralny 14, Wroc-
    law, Poland (Roman Catholic).   992

Portugal
SEMINARIO EPISCOPAL.   Angra, Island Azores, Portu-
    gal (Roman Catholic).   993
SEMINARIO CONCILIAR.   Rua de Santa Margarida,
    Brago, Portugal (Roman Catholic).   994
SEMINARIO MAIOR DE BRANGANCA.   Branganca,
    Portugal (Roman Catholic).   995
SEMINARIO MAIOR.   Coimbra, Portugal (Roman
    Catholic).   996

SEMINARIO MAIOR DE N. S. DA PURIFICACAO.
Evora, Portugal (Roman Catholic). 997
SEMINARIO DIOCESANO. Rua de S. Lucia, Funchal
(Madeira) Portugal (Roman Catholic). 998
SEMINARIO MAIOR. Guarda, Portugal (Roman Catho-
lic). 999
SEMINARIO MAIOR. Lamego, Portugal (Roman Catho-
lic). 1000
SEMINARIO MAIOR DE N.S. DA CONCEICAO. Leiria,
Portugal (Roman Catholic). 1001
SEMINARIO MAIOR PATRIARCAL DE CRISTO REI.
Olivais (Lisbon) Portugal (Roman Catholic). 1002
SEMINARIO DE N. S. DA CONCEICAO. Se (Oporto)
Portugal (Roman Catholic). 1003
SEMINARIO MAIOR DE IMAC. CORACAO DE MARIA.
Portalegre, Portugal (Roman Catholic). 1004
SEMINARIO MAIOR N. S. DA ESPERANCA. Rua 5 de
Outubro, Viseu (Beirs Alta) Portugal (Roman Catho-
lic). 1005
SEMINARIO MAIOR. Rua do Carvalho 1, Vita Real de
Tras os Montes, Vita Real, Portugal (Roman Catho-
lic). 1006

Rumania
SEMINARUL TEOLOGIC GRECO-UNIT DIN ALBA JULIA.
Blaj, Rumania (Orthodox). 1007
INSTITUTUL TEOLOGIC UNIVERSITAR. Rue Sf. Ecate-
rina, 2 Raion N. Balescu, Bucharest, Rumania (East-
ern Orthodox--Patriarchate of Romania). 1008
SEMINARUL TEOLOGIC. Buzau, Raion Buzau, Regiunea
Ploiesti, Rumania (Orthodox--Patriarchate of Roman-
ia). 1009
SEMINARUL TEOLOGIC. Caransebes, Raion Caransebes,
Regiunea Banat, Rumania (Orthodox--Patriarchate of
Romania). 1010
FAKULTAT DE TEOLOGIC REFORMATA BIBLIOTECA.
Piata Malinowski 13, Cluj, Rumania (Reformed). 1011
SEMINARUL TEOLOGIC. Cluj, Piata Victoriei nr. 18,
Rumania (Orthodox--Patriarchate of Romania). 1012
MITROPOLIA MOLDOVEI SI SRECEVEII. Strasses
Stefan cel Mare 46, Iasi, Rumania. 1013
SEMINARUL TEOLOGIC. M-REA NEAMT, Raionul Tg-
Neamt, Regiunea Bacau, Nr. 1.448, Rumania (Ortho-
dox--Patriarchate of Romania). 1014
SEMINARUL TEOLOGIC. Mofleni-Craiova, Raion Craio-
va, Regiunea Oltenia, Rumania (Orthodox-Patriarchate
of Romania). 1015

Rumania (cont.)
INSTITUTUL TEOLOGIC DE GRAD UNIVERSITAR.
   Strasse 1 Mai nr. 20, Sibiu, Rumania (Orthodox--
   Patriarchate of Romania).   1016
S. H. HERRN BISCHOF DR. FRIEDRICH MULLER
   PROTESTANTISCHE-THEOLOGISCHE INSTITUT--
   LUTHERNSCHE FAKULTAT. G'Ral Maghern 4,
   Sibiu-Hermannstadt, Rumania (Lutheran).   1017

Russia
LENINGRAD ECCLESIASTICAL ACADEMY AND SEMI-
   NARY. C-167, Olodovney Kanal 17, Leningrad,
   Russia, U.S.S.R. (Orthodox--Patriarchate of Mos-
   cow).   1018
ABBEY OF ST. SERGIUS. Moscow, Russia, U.S.S.R.
   (Eastern Orthodox).   1019
HOLY TRINITY SEMINARY. Moscow, Russia,
   U.S.S.R. (Eastern Orthodox).   1020
MOSCOW ECCLESIASTICAL ACADEMY AND SEMINARY.
   Moscow Region, Trinity-Cyprian Lavra, Zagorsk,
   Moscow, Russia, U.S.S.R. (Orthodox--Patriarchate
   of Moscow).   1021
OBLATE LAVRA AKADEMIA. Moscow, Russia,
   U.S.S.R. (Eastern Orthodox).   1022
ODESSA ECCLESIASTICAL SEMINARY. Odessa, Russia,
   U.S.S.R. (Orthodox--Patriarchate of Moscow).   1023
S. H. HERRN ERZBISCHOF JEAN KUVIT. Raamatuks-
   gustrasse 8, Estland, Tallinn I, Russia, U.S.S.R.
   (Lutheran).   1024

Scotland
ABERDEEN UNIVERSITY--KING'S COLLEGE. Aberdeen,
   Scotland (Interdenominational) 1495.
   Library: 1495, OB, OS, ___-25,000, E, DDC, SC,
   ___-50   1025
CHRIST COLLEGE. 2 Alford Place, Aberdeen, Scot-
   land (Church of Scotland--Presbyterian).   1026
ST. PETER'S COLLEGE. Cardross, Dumbarton, Scot-
   land (Roman Catholic).   1027
EDINBURGH THEOLOGICAL COLLEGE. Roseberry
   College, Edinburgh 12, Scotland (Anglican).   1028
THEOLOGICAL COLLEGE OF THE SCOTTISH EPISCO-
   PAL CHURCH. Roseberry Crescent, Edinburgh 12,
   Scotland (Scottish Episcopal Church).   1029
UNIVERSITY OF EDINBURGH--NEW COLLEGE. The
   Mound, Edinburgh, Scotland (Church of Scotland--
   Presbyterian) 1846.   1030

UNIVERSITY OF GLASGOW. Glasgow W 2, Scotland
  (Independent) 1451.   1031
ST. ANDREW'S COLLEGE. Drygrange, Melrose, Rox-
  burghshire, Scotland (Roman Catholic--Diocese of
  St. Andrew's and Edinburgh) 1953.
    Library: 1953, 0, OB, OS, 40,000-15,000, E, own,
    F-S, SC, 20-6   1032
UNIVERSITY OF ST. ANDREWS. St. Andrews, Scotland
  (Church of Scotland) 1411.
    Library: 1411, 35, OB, OS, 550,000-520,000, E,
    LC, F-S, SC, 3,000-2,900, Ar Sl Mi Pi Ma Mu   1033

Spain
SEMINARIO MAYOR. Albacete, Spain (Roman Catholic).1034
FACULTAD DE FILOSOFIA S. J. Apartado 10, Alcala
  de Henares (Madrid) Spain (Roman Catholic--Society
  of Jesus) 1932.
    Library: 1932, 7, OB, OS, 200,000-50,000, S,
    Decimal, F-S, 250-250   1035
SEMINARIO CONCILIAR. San Buenaventura 9, Alcala
  de Henares (Madrid) Spain (Roman Catholic).   1036
SEMINARIO MAYOR. Carretera de Hijar, Almeria,
  Spain (Roman Catholic).   1037
SEMINARIO MAYOR. Astorga (Leon) Spain (Roman
  Catholic).   1038
SEMINARIO CONCILIAR. Apartado 24, Avila, Spain
  (Roman Catholic).   1039
SEMINARIO MAYOR DIOCESANO. Apartado 88, Bada-
  joz, Spain (Roman Catholic).   1040
SEMINARIO CONCILIAR. Barbastro (Huesca) Spain
  (Roman Catholic).   1041
S. FRANCISCO DE BORJA--FACULTAD TEOLOGICA.
  San Cugat del Valles (Barcelona) Spain (Roman
  Catholic) 1898.
    Library: 1898, 4, OB, OS, 700,000-300,000, S,
    SC, 220-170, Fi   1042
SEMINARIO CONCILIAR. Diputacion 231, Barcelona,
  Spain (Roman Catholic).   1043
SEMINARIO CONCILIAR--VICH. Barcelona, Spain
  (Roman Catholic) 1735.
    Library: 1735, 0, OB, 16,000-10,000, L, A-Z by
    subject, F-S, SC, 30-___   1044
SEMINARIO DIOCESANO. Bilbao, Spain (Roman Catho-
  lic).   1045
COLEGIO MAXIMO DE SAN FRANCISCO XAVIER--
  SEMINARIO METROPOLITANO. Burgos, Ona, Spain

Spain (cont.)
  (Roman Catholic) 1881.   1046
SEMINARIO MAYOR.   Caceres, Spain (Roman Catho-
  lic).   1047
SEMINARIO DIOCESANO.   Priu 1, Cadiz, Spain (Ro-
  man Catholic).   1048
SEMINARIO DIOCESANO.   Carretera Zaragoza en Lo-
  grono, Calahorra, Spain (Roman Catholic).   1049
SEMINARIO MAYOR.   Plaza de Apostoles, Cartagena
  (Murcia) Spain (Roman Catholic).   1050
UNIVERSIDAD PONTIFICIA DE COMILLAS--FACULTY
  OF THEOLOGY.   Comillas, Spain (Roman Catholic--
  Society of Jesus) 1935, 1904.   1051
SEMINARIO MAYOR.   Avenida de los Martires 20,
  Ciudad Real, Spain (Roman Catholic).   1052
SEMINARIO CONCILIAR.   Plaza de Herrasti 1, Ciudad
  Rodrigo, Spain (Roman Catholic).   1053
SEMINARIO CONCILIAR.   Obispo Villa 9, Ciudadela
  (Menorca) Spain (Roman Catholic).   1054
SEMINARIO CONCILIAR.   Apartado 15, Cordoba, Spain
  (Roman Catholic).   1055
SEMINARIO CONCILIAR.   Cuenca, Spain (Roman
  Catholic).   1056
SEMINARIO MAYOR.   El Burgo de Osma (Soria)
  Spain (Roman Catholic).   1057
SEMINARIO CONCILIAR.   Gerona, Spain (Roman Catho-
  lic--Diocesis de Gerona) 1516.
  Library: 3, OB, OS, 25,000-25,000, L S, Decimal,
  F-S, SC, Ar Ma Mu   1058
FACULTAD DE TEOLOGIA.   Apartado 32, Paseo de
  Cartuja, Granada, Spain (Roman Catholic--Society of
  Jesus) 1939.
  Library: 1939, 2, OB, 84,000-83,701, G L S, A-Z
  by authors, F-S, 365-350, Sl Mi   1059
PONTIFICIO Y REAL SEMINARIO MAYOR.   Carretera
  de Alfacar, Granada, Spain (Roman Catholic).   1060
SEMINARIO METROPOLITANO.   Carretera de Fargue
  en Granada, Guadix, Spain (Roman Catholic).   1061
SEMINARIO MAYOR.   Plaza de la Universidad 6,
  Huesca (Huesca) Spain (Roman Catholic).   1062
SEMINARIO MAYOR.   Juan Roman 2, Ibiza (Baleares)
  Spain (Roman Catholic).   1063
SEMINARIO MAYOR.   Jaca (Huesca) Spain (Roman
  Catholic).   1064
SEMINARIO MAYOR.   Jaen, Spain (Roman Catholic).   1065
SEMINARIO MAYOR.   C. Sta. Domingo, La Laguna
  de Tenerife, La Laguna, Spain (Roman Catholic)   1066

SEMINARIO DIOCESANO.   Doctor Chil 25, Las Palmas
de Gran Carraria, Las Palmas, Spain (Roman Catho-
lic).   1067
SEMINARIO MAYOR.   Leon, Spain (Roman Catholic).   1068
SEMINARIO MAYOR.   Rambla de Aragon 37, Lerida,
Spain (Roman Catholic).   1069
SEMINARIO CONCILIAR.   Avenida a Lopez Perez 2,
Lugo, Spain (Roman Catholic).   1070
SEMINARIO CONCILIAR.   Apartado 190, Malaga, Spain
(Roman Catholic).   1071
SEMINARIO REAL Y CONCILIAR.   Mondonedo, Spain
(Roman Catholic).   1072
SEMINARIO DIOCESANO.   Vista Hermosa, Apartado 16,
Orense, Spain (Roman Catholic).   1073
SEMINARIO MAYOR.   Orihuela (Alicante) Spain (Roman
Catholic).   1074
SEMINARIO DE LA ASUNCION.   Apartado 157, Oviedo,
Spain (Roman Catholic).   1075
SEMINARIO CONCILIAR.   Almaraz 4, Palencia, Spain
(Roman Catholic).   1076
SEMINARIO CONCILIAR.   Seminario 4, Palma de Mal-
lorca, Palma, Spain (Roman Catholic).   1077
SEMINARIO CONCILIAR.   Avenida de la Franco, Pamp-
lona, Spain (Roman Catholic).   1078
SEMINARIO DIOCESANO.   Plaza de la Cathedral, Pla-
sencia, Spain (Roman Catholic).   1079
PONTIFICIA FACULTAD TEOLOGICA DE SAN ESTEBAN.
Convento de San Esteban, Apartado 17, Salamanca,
Spain (Roman Catholic) 1947.   1080
UNIVERSIDAD PONTIFICIA DE SALAMANCA--SEMI-
NARIO MAYOR.   Calle Compania 1, Apartado 23,
Salamanca, Spain (Roman Catholic) 1940.   1081
UNIVERSIDAD PONTIFICIA DE SALAMANCA--INSTI-
TUTE OF PASTORAL STUDIES.   Calle Compania,
Salamanca, Spain (Roman Catholic) 1940.   1082
SEMINARIO MAYOR.   San Sebastian, Spain (Roman
Catholic).   1083
UNIVERSIDAD PONTIFICIA DE COMILLAS--SEMINARIO
DIOCESANO.   Monte Corsaobian, Apartado 267, San-
tander, Spain (Roman Catholic).   1084
SEMINARIO CONCILIAR.   Plaza de la Immaculadad 5,
Santiago de Compostela, Santiago, Spain (Roman
Catholic).   1085
SEMINARIO.   Segarbe (Castellion) Spain (Roman Catho-
lic).   1086
SEMINARIO DIOCESANO.   Apartado 4, Segovia, Spain
(Roman Catholic).   1087

Spain (cont.)
SEMINARIO MAYOR.   Seville, Spain (Roman Catholic)
1900.
    Library: 1900, 0, OB, OS, 12,000-10,000, L S,
    Decimal, F-S, 30-   1088
SEMINARIO DIOCESAÑO.   Apartado 1, Siguenza (Guada-
lajara) Spain (Roman Catholic).   1089
SEMINARIO MAYOR.   Solsona (Lerido) Spain (Roman
Catholic).   1090
SEMINARIO CONCILIAR.   Puente Cristo, Tarazona
(Zaragosa) Spain (Roman Catholic).   1091
SEMINARIO CONCILIAR PONTIFICIO.   Calle San Pablo
4, Tarragona, Spain (Roman Catholic).   1092
SEMINARIO CONCILIAR.   Plaza de Perez Prado 1,
Teruel, Spain (Roman Catholic).   1093
SEMINARIO METROPOLITANO.   Plaza de San Andres,
Toledo, Spain (Roman Catholic).   1094
SEMINARIO DIOCESANO.   Apartado 68, Tortosa, Spain
(Roman Catholic).   1095
SEMINARIO DIOCESANO.   Calvo Sotelo 4, Tuy (Ponte-
vedra) Spain (Roman Catholic).   1096
SEMINARIO DIOCESANO.   Urgel (Lerida 1) Spain
(Roman Catholic).   1097
SEMINARIO METROPOLITANO.   Valencia, Spain (Roman
Catholic).   1098
SEMINARIO DIOCESANO.   Sanz y Fores 1, Valladolid,
Spain (Roman Catholic).   1099
SEMINARIO DIOCESANO.   Apartado 86, Vitoria, Spain
(Roman Catholic).   1100
SEMINARIO DIOCESANO.   Zamora, Spain (Roman Catho-
lic).   1101
SEMINARIO METROPOLITANO.   Zaragosa, Spain (Roman
Catholic).   1102

Sweden
LUNDS UNIVERSITET--FACULTY OF THEOLOGY.
Sandgaten 1, Lund, Sweden (Lutheran) 1682.   1103
STOCKHOLMS TEOLOGISHA INSTITUT.   Vardshus-
backen 1, Stockholm, Sweden (Lutheran).   1104
KINGLIGA UNIVERSITET--UPPSALA FACULTY OF
THEOLOGY.   Uppsala, Sweden (Lutheran) 1477.   1105

Switzerland
THEOLOGISCHEN SEMINARS DER UNIVERSITAT.   CH-
4051 Basel, Nadelberg 10, Switzerland (Evangelical
Reformed Church) 1910.
    Library: 1910, 1, 50,000-25,000, G, own, F-S,

97-92, Sl Ma   1106
UNIVERSITAT BASEL--FACULTY OF THEOLOGY.
Petersplatz, Basel, Switzerland (Roman Catholic)
1460.   1107
UNIVERSITAT BERN--EVANGELISCH-THEOLOGISCHEN
SEMINARS. Sidlerstrasse 4, 3000 Bern, Switzerland
(Government) 1834.
Library: 1834, 1, OS, 10,000-7,000, G, F-S,
36-   1108
UNIVERSITAT BERN--FACULTY OF CATHOLIC THE-
OLOGY. Bern, Switzerland (Roman Catholic) 1528.   1109
UNIVERSITAT BERN--OLD CATHOLIC FACULTY. Bern,
Switzerland (Old Catholic Church) 1528.   1110
PRIESTERSEMINAR ST. LUZI.   CH-7000 Chur, Switz-
erland (Roman Catholic--Priesterseminar St. Luzi
des Bistums Chur) 1800.
Library: 1800, 1, OS, 50,000-42,000, G, own, F-
S, 82-76   1111
GRAND SEMINAIRE. Fribourg, Switzerland (Roman
Catholic).   1112
UNIVERSITE DE FRIBOURG--FACULTY OF THEOLOGY.
Fribourg, Switzerland (Roman Catholic) 1889.   1113
UNIVERSITE DE GENEVE. Cour des Bastions, Geneva,
Switzerland (Protestant--Calvinist) 1559.   1114
WORLD COUNCIL OF CHURCHES. 150, route de Fer-
ney, 1211 Geneva 20, Switzerland (General Secretariat
of World Council of Churches) 1946.
Library: 1946, 4, OS, 120,000-42,000, DDC, SC,
650-450, Ar Fi Sl Mi Pi   1115
UNIVERSITE DE LAUSANNE-- FACULTY OF PROTES-
TANT THEOLOGY. Palais de Rumine, Lausanne,
Switzerland, 1537.   1116
SEMINARIO "S. CARLO." Lugano, Switzerland (Roman
Catholic).   1117
PRIESTERSEMINAR ST. BEAT. Hof (Luzerne) Switzer-
land (Roman Catholic).   1118
SEMINAIRE DE THEOLOGIE. 26, av. du 1er, Mars,
2000 Neuchetel, Switzerland (Eglise Reformee--
Evangelique du Canton de Neuchetel) 1847.
Library: 1847, 2, OB, OS, 5,000-4,000, F G, A-
Z, F-S, 45-40   1119
PRIESTERSEMINAR ST. GEORGEN. St. Gallen, Switz-
erland (Roman Catholic).   1120
GRAND SEMINAIRE. 1950 Sion, Switzerland (Roman
Catholic) 1950.
Library: 4, OB, 13,000-12,000, F L, own, F-S,
SC, 39-35   1121

Switzerland (cont.)
PRIESTERSEMINAR ST. JOHANN.   Solothurn, Switz-
   erland (Roman Catholic) 1927.
   Library: 1927, 1, OS, 5,000-3,000, G, own,
   F-S, 30-   1122
BIBLIOTHEQUE PUBLIQUE ET UNIVERSITAIRE.
   Ville de Geneve, Switzerland (Government) 1559.
   Library: SC   1123
INTERNATIONAL BAPTIST THEOLOGICAL LIBRARY.
   Ruschlikon, Zurich, Switzerland (Southern Baptist
   F.M.B., Richmond, Virginia) 1949.
   Library: 1949, 1, OB, OS, 50,000-22,000, E G,
   DDC, F-S, 389-80, Mi Pi Ma VF   1124
UNIVERSITEIT ZURICH--FACULTY OF THEOLOGY.
   Ranistrasse 71, Zurich, Switzerland (Reformed)
   1523.   1125

Wales
ABERYSTWYTH THEOLOGICAL COLLEGE.   Aberyst-
   wyth, Cardiganshire, Wales (Presbyterian Church of
   Wales) 1875.
   Library: 1906, 1, OS, 30,000-25,000, E, own,
   30-3 Ar   1126
UNIVERSITY COLLEGE OF NORTH WALES--BANGOR
   SCHOOL OF THEOLOGY.   Bangor, Wales (Interde-
   nominational) 1884.   1127
NORTH WALES BAPTIST COLLEGE.   Bangor, Caernar-
   vonshire, Wales (Baptist Union of Great Britain and
   Ireland, Baptist Union of Wales).   1128
ST. MICHAEL'S THEOLOGICAL COLLEGE.   Llandaff,
   Cardiff, Wales (Anglican--The Church in Wales) 1892.
   Library: 1892, 0, OB, OS, 10,000-8,200, E Welsh,
   own, F-S, 20-20   1129
SOUTH WALES BAPTIST COLLEGE.   Richmond Road,
   Cardiff, Wales (Baptist Union of Great Britain and
   Ireland).   1130
UNIVERSITY COLLEGE OF SOUTH WALES AND MON-
   MOUTHSHIRE--CARDIFF SCHOOL OF THEOLOGY.
   Cathays Park, Cardiff, Wales (Interdenominational)
   1883.   1131
ST. DAVID'S COLLEGE--BISHOP THOMAS BURGESS
   THEOLOGICAL HALL.   Lampeter, Cardiganshire,
   Wales (Anglican) 1822.   1132
CONGREGATIONAL MEMORIAL COLLEGE.   Swansea,
   Glam., Wales (Congregational Churches) 1757.
   Library: 1757, 1, OB, OS, ___-28,000, E Welsh,
   DDC, F-S, 30-18   1133

Yugoslavia
BOGOSLOSKII FAKULTET SRPSKE PRAVOSLAVNA
   CRKVE. 7 juli br. 2, Belgrade, Yugoslavia (East-
   ern Orthodox).   1134
BOGOSLOVIJA SVETOG SAVE. Mije Kovaceivca 11,
   Belgrade, Yugoslavia (Serbian Orthdox Church).   1135
KNJIZNICA VISOKE BOGOSLOVNE SKOLE. Knjiznica
   V.B.S., Strossmayerov trg 5, Djakovo, Yugoslavia
   (Roman Catholic) 1806.
   Library: 1806, 5, OB, OS, 45,000-5,000, Croatian
   F G L, F-S, 22-2   1136
SRPSKE PRAVOSLAVNA BOGOSLOVIJA. Manistir Krka
   p. Kistanje, Dalmatia, Yugoslavia (Serbian Orthodox).1137
SEMINARIO MAGGIORE. Ljubljana, Yugoslavia (Roman
   Catholic).   1138
BAPTIST THEOLOGICAL SEMINARY. Novi Sad, Yugo-
   slavia (Baptist) 1954, 1967.   1139
SEMINARIUM MAIUS. Ul. Stanka Jekica 6, Pazin
   (Istra) Yugoslavia (Roman Catholic).   1140
SRYESKA PRAVOSLAVNA BOGOSLOVIJA. Prizren,
   Yugoslavia (Serbian Orthodox).   1141
BOGOSLOVIJA SVETOG SAVE. Sremski Karlova, Yugo-
   slavia (Serbian Orthodox).   1142
SEMINARIUM MAIUS. Trg. 27 Marta 2, Zadar (Dal-
   matia) Yugoslavia (Roman Catholic).   1143
SEMINARIUM MAIUS. Kaptol 29, Zagreb, Yugoslavia
   (Roman Catholic).   1144

North America

Canada
  Alberta
CHRISTIAN TRAINING INSTITUTE. 10810 78th Avenue,
    Edmonton, Alberta, Canada (North America Baptist
    Convention).   1145
ST. STEPHEN'S COLLEGE--UNITED CHURCH THEO-
    LOGICAL COLLEGE. University of Alberta Campus,
    Edmonton, Alberta, Canada (United Church of Canada)
    1909.
    Library: 1909, 1, OS, 14,000-11,000, E, DDC, SC,
    60-0, Ar Mi Pi Ma Mu VF   1146

  British Columbia
ANGLICAN THEOLOGICAL COLLEGE OF BRITISH
    COLUMBIA. 6050 Chancellor Drive, Vancouver,
    British Columbia 8, Canada (Anglican) 1910.   1147
UNION COLLEGE OF BRITISH COLUMBIA. 6000 Iona
    Drive, Vancouver 8, British Columbia, Canada (United
    Church of Canada) 1927.
    Library: 1927, 2, OB, OS, 60,000-23,000, E,
    LC, 133-___, Ar Mi   1148

  Manitoba
UNIVERSITY OF MANITOBA--ST. JOHN'S COLLEGE.
    Winnipeg 19, Manitoba, Canada (Anglican Church
    of Canada) 1867.
    Library: 1867, 1, OB, 22,000-21,000, E, DDC,
    SC, 185-130   1149

  Newfoundland
QUEENS COLLEGE. St. John's, Newfoundland, Canada
    (Anglican) 1841.   1150

  Nova Scotia
HOLY HEART SEMINARY. 6155 Quinpool Road, Halifax,
    Nova Scotia, Canada (Roman Catholic) 1895.
    Library: 1895, 1, OB, OS, 10,000-10,000, DDC,
    F-S, 70-45   1151

PINE HILL DIVINITY HALL. 640 Francklyn Street,
Halifax, Nova Scotia, Canada (United Church of
Canada) 1820.   1152
ST. MARY'S UNIVERSITY. 5932 Inglis Street, Halifax,
Nova Scotia, Canada (Roman Catholic--Society of
Jesus) 1802.   1153
UNIVERSITY OF KING'S COLLEGE. Coburg Road,
Halifax, Nova Scotia, Canada (Anglican Church of
Canada) 1789.
   Library: 1802, 1, OS, 45,000-50,000 E, LC, F-S,
   SC, 115-50   1154
ACADIA UNIVERSITY--SCHOOL OF THEOLOGY. Wolf-
ville, Nova Scotia, Canada (United Baptist Conven-
tion of the Atlantic Province) 1838.   1155

Ontario
SCHOLASTICATE ST.-JEAN. 431 Montreal Road, Zone
7, Eastview, Ontario, Canada (Roman Catholic--
Montfort Fathers) 1903.
   Library: 1903, 3, OB, OS, 15,000-15,000, F, A-
   Z and Numbers, F-S, 60-45   1156
McMASTER UNIVERSITY--McMASTER DIVINITY COL-
LEGE. Hamilton, Ontario, Canada (Baptist Conven-
tion of Ontario and Quebec) 1887.   1157
QUEEN'S THEOLOGICAL COLLEGE. Kingston, Ontario,
Canada (United Church of Canada) 1841.   1158
HURON COLLEGE. London, Ontario, Canada (Anglican
Church of Canada) 1863.
   Library: 1863, 3, OB, OS, 100,000-58,000, E F,
   LC, 250-75, Mi   1159
SEAGER HALL. London, Ontario, Canada (Anglican).   1160
MT. CARMEL COLLEGE. Niagara Falls, Ontario,
Canada (Roman Catholic--Order of Carmelites)
1925.   1161
BIBLIOTHEQUE DES PP. CAPUCINS. 1062 Wellington,
Ottawa 3, Ontario, Canada (Roman Catholic--Les
Peres Capucins).
   Library: 1910, 1, OB, OS, 25,000-20,000, F, own,
   F-S, 40-   1162
HOLY ROSARY SCHOLASTICATE. Box 452, Ottawa,
Zone 2, Ontario, Canada (Roman Catholic).   1163
OTTAWA MAJOR SEMINARY (ST. THOMAS ACQUINAS
SEMINARY). 1245 Kilborn Avenue, Ottawa 8, On-
tario, Canada (Roman Catholic) 1848.
   Library: 1957, 2, OB, 45,000-25,000, E F, Vatican,
   F-S, 106-106   1164
ST. JOHN SCHOLASTICATE. 431 Montreal Road, Otta-

Ontario (cont.)
wa 7, Ontario, Canada (Roman Catholic--The Mont-
fort Fathers: Company of Mary) 1903.
Library: 1903, 3, OB, OS, 15,000-15,000, F,
A-Z, F-S, 60-45   1165
SCHOLASTICATE ST. JOSEPH. Avenue des Oblates,
Ottawa 1, Ontario, Canada (Roman Catholic--Mis-
sionary Oblates of Mary Immaculate) 1885.
Library: 1885, 1, OB, 90,000-75,000 F, LC,
F-S, SC, 225-___, Ar   1166
SEMINAIRE ABBOT DE MAZENOD. 623 Smyth Road,
Ottawa, Zone 8, Ontario, Canada (Roman Catholic)
1960.   1167
ST. AUGUSTINE'S SEMINARY. 2661 Kingston Road,
Scarborough, Ontario, Canada (Roman Catholic--
Archdiocese of Toronto) 1913.
Library: 1913, 1, OB, OS, 100,000-20,000, E,
LC, F-S, SC, 210-150, Mi Ma VF   1168
ST. FRANCIS XAVIER SEMINARY. 2685 Kingston
Road, Scarborough, Ontario, Canada (Roman Cath-
olic--Scarborough Foreign Mission Society) 1924.
Library: 1924, 4, OB, OS, 10,000-5,000, E, own,
F-S, 20-___   1169
VICTORIA UNIVERSITY--EMMANUEL COLLEGE. 75
Queen's Park Crescent, Toronto 5, Ontario, Canada
(United Church of Canada) 1925.   1170
KNOX COLLEGE. 59 St. George Street, Toronto, On-
tario, Canada (Presbyterian Church in Canada) 1845.
Caven Library.   1171
PONTIFICAL INSTITUTE OF MEDIEVAL STUDIES. 59
Queen's Park Crescent, Toronto, Zone 5, Ontario
Canada (Roman Catholic) 1929.   1172
ST. BASIL'S SEMINARY. 95 St. Joseph Street, Toronto
5, Ontario, Canada (Roman Catholic--Congregation of
St. Basil) 1894.
Library: 1894, 1, OB, OS, 50,000-35,000, E, LC,
200-175   1173
UNIVERSITY OF TORONTO--ST. MICHAEL'S COLLEGE.
Toronto, Ontario, Canada (Roman Catholic) 1852.   1174
UNIVERSITY OF TRINITY COLLEGE--FACULTY OF
DIVINITY. Hoskin Avenue, Toronto 5, Ontario,
Canada (Anglican Church of Canada) 1852.
Library: 1852, 1, OB, OS, 50,000-24,325, E,
LC, 50-45, Sl Mi Pi   1175
WYCLIFFE COLLEGE. Toronto 5, Ontario, Canada
(Anglican Church of Canada) 1877.
Leonard Library: 1939, 1, OB, OS, 28,000-27,500,

E, LC, SC, 90-20, Mi Ma   1176
WATERLOO LUTHERAN SEMINARY. Waterloo, Ontario,
  Canada (Lutheran Church in America--Eastern Canada
  Synod) 1911.
  Library: 1911, 4, OB, OS, 90,000-17,800, E F G
  Scandinavian, LC, F-S, 225-___, Mi Mu VF   1177
CANTERBURY COLLEGE. 172 Patricia Road, Windsor,
  Ontario, Canada (Anglican) 1957.   1178
HOLY REDEEMER COLLEGE. Windsor, Ontario, Canada
  (Roman Catholic--Congregation of the Most Holy Re-
  deemer) 1958.
  Library: 1958, 1, OB, OS, 50,000-36,000, E, LC,
  115-105, Ar   1179
IONA COLLEGE. Windsor, Ontario, Canada (United
  Church of Canada) 1964.   1180
UNIVERSITY OF WINDSOR--ASSUMPTION UNIVERSITY.
  400 Huron Line, Windsor, Ontario, Canada (Roman
  Catholic) 1857.   1181

  Quebec
DIOCESAN COLLEGE OF MONTREAL. 3473 University
  Street, Montreal, Quebec, Canada (Roman Catholic)
  1873.   1182
GRAND SEMINAIRE DE MONTREAL. 2065 Ouest, Rue
  Sherbrooke, Montreal 25, Quebec, Canada (Roman
  Catholic--Society of St. Sulpice) 1840.
  Library: 1840, 4, OB, 80,000-82,000, F, DDC,
  F-S, SC, 350-225   1183
McGILL UNIVERSITY--FACULTY OF DIVINITY. 3520
  University Street, Montreal 2, Quebec, Canada (Inter-
  denominational) 1948.
  Divinity Hall Library: 1948, 2-1/2, OB, OS, 80,000-
  60,000, E, Cutter, 189-___, Ar   1184
PRESBYTERIAN COLLEGE. 3495 University Street,
  Montreal, Quebec, Canada (Presbyterian Church in
  Canada) 1867.
  Library: 1867, 1, OB, OS, 35,000-20,400, E,
  Cutter, 40-15, Ar   1185
SCHOLASTICATE CENTRAL DE MONTREAL. 7000
  Marie Victoria Street, Montreal, Zone 39, Quebec,
  Canada (Roman Catholic).   1186
SCHOLASTICATE-ECOLE NORMALE DES F. E. C.
  Pavilion-de-la-Salle, 7225 Marie Victoria Street,
  Montreal, Zone 39, Quebec, Canada (Roman Catho-
  lic) 1930.   1187
SCHOLASTICATE SAINT PIUS X. 2900 Chemin Saint
  Catherine, Montreal, Zone 26, Quebec, Canada

Quebec (cont.)
(Roman Catholic).   1188
SEMINAIRE DE PHILOSOPHIE. 3888 Chemin Cote de
Neiges, Montreal, Zone 25, Quebec, Canada (Roman
Catholic) 1880.   1189
SEMINAIRE DE STE. CROIX. 635 Ste. Croix, Montreal,
Quebec, Canada (Roman Catholic).   1190
SEMINAIRE ST. SACRAMENT. 167 rue Saint Louis,
Montreal, Quebec, Canada (Roman Catholic).   1191
SOEURS GRESES DE MONTREAL. 1190 rue Guy, Mon-
treal, Zone 25, Quebec, Canada (Roman Catholic).
Maison Mere Library.   1192
UNITED THEOLOGICAL COLLEGE. 3472 University
Street, Montreal, Quebec, Canada (United Church of
Canada) 1926.   1193
UNIVERSITY OF MONTREAL--PIUS XI INSTITUTE.
2065 Sherbrook Street West, Montreal, Quebec, Can-
ada (Roman Catholic) 1896.   1194
SCHOLASTICATE DES SS. DE NOTRE DAME DU ST.
ROSAIRE. Avenue du Rosaire, Quebec, Quebec,
Canada (Roman Catholic) 1932.   1195
SEMINAIRE DES PERES MARISTES. 2315 Chemin St.
Louis, Sillery, Quebec 6, Quebec, Canada (Roman
Catholic).   1196
UNIVERSITE LAVAL--SECTEUR THEOLOGIE. Cite
Universitaire, Saint-Foy, Quebec 10, Quebec, Canada
(Roman Catholic--Secular Clergy) 1852.
Library: 1852, 2, OB, OS, 100,000-25,000 F, LC,
F-S, 220-   1197
SEMINAIRE DE RIMOUSKI. Rimouski, Quebec, Canada
(Roman Catholic).   1198
SEMINAIRE ST. ALPHONSE. St. Anne-de-Beaupre,
Quebec, Canada (Roman Catholic).   1199
ABBAYE SAINT-BENOIT DU LAC. Province de Quebec,
Canada (Roman Catholic--Benedictine Monks) 1912.
Library: 1912, 4, OB, OS, ___-75,000, F L, LC,
F-S, 110-75, Ar Ma Mu   1200
PRIEURE DES PERES PREMONTRES. St. Bernard-
de-Lacolle, Comte de St. Jean, Province de Quebec,
Canada (Roman Catholic--The Norbertine Order) 1949.
Library: 1949, 1, OB, OS, 3,000-3,000, F, CDV,
30-25, Ar VF   1201
SEMINAIRE DE SAINT JEAN. Boulevard Montcalm,
Box 350, Saint Jean, Quebec, Canada (Roman Catho-
lic).   1202
SEMINAIRE DE SAINTE THERESE. Sainte Therese de
Blainville, Quebec, Canada (Roman Catholic) 1825.

Library: 1825, 7, OS, 300,000-70,000, F, DDC,
F-S, 280-160, Sl Ma Mu   1203
SEMINAIRE DU SACRE COEUR. Saint Victor Station,
Saint Victor de Beauce, Quebec, Canada (Roman
Catholic).   1204
GRAND SEMINAIRE DES SAINT APOTRES. 500 rue
Murray, Sherbrooke, Quebec, Canada (Roman Catho-
lic) 1954.   1205
MONASTERE DES PERES REDEMPTORISTS. 871 rue
Ontario, Sherbrooke, Quebec, Canada (Roman Catho-
lic) 1954.   1206
SEMINAIRE SAINT SACRAMENT. Terrebonne, Quebec,
Canada (Roman Catholic).   1207
GRAND SEMINAIRE TROIS RIVIERES. 3600 Ste. Mar-
guerite, Trois Rivieres, Quebec, Canada (Roman
Catholic--Clerge Diocesan) 1964.
Library: 1964, 0, OB, OS, 50,000-5,000, F, UDC,
150-   1208
SEMINAIRE SAINT ANTOINE. 3351 Boulevard des
Forges, Trois Rivieres, Quebec, Canada (Roman
Catholic) 1914.
Library: 1960, 4, OB, 70,000-59,000, F, DDC,
SC, 350-   , Sl Ma Mu   1209
SEMINAIRE ST. JOSEPH. Rue Lavioletee, Box 548,
Trois Rivieres, Quebec, Canada (Roman Catholic)
1860.   1210
SEMINAIRE DES MISSIONS-ETRANGERES. 60 rue
Desnoyers, Ville de Laval, Quebec, Canada (Roman
Catholic--Societe des Missions-Etrangeres du Quebec)
1924.
Library: 1924, 1, OB, OS, 50,000-20,495, F,
DDC, F-S, 108-67   1211

Saskatchewan
COLLEGE OF EMMANUEL AND ST. CHAD. Saska-
toon, Saskatchewan, Canada (Anglican Church of
Canada) 1964.
Library: 1879, 2, OB, 20,000-13,000, E, DDC,
SC, 20-5, Ar Sl   1212
LUTHERAN THEOLOGICAL SEMINARY. 1502 Eighth
Street, Saskatoon, Saskatchewan, Canada (Lutheran
Church in America, Evangelical Lutheran Church of
Canada) 1914.
Berkey Memorial Library: 1914, 2, OB, OS,
20,000-19,000, E, LC, F-S, SC, 108-52, VF   1213
ST. ANDREW'S COLLEGE. Saskatoon, Saskatchewan,
Canada (United Church of Canada) 1912.   1214

United States of America

Alabama
ASSUMPTION HALL--JESUIT HOUSE OF STUDIES.
3659 Loyola Lane, Mobile, Alabama 36608 U. S. A.
(Roman Catholic--Society of Jesus) 1937.   1215

Arkansas
JACKSON THEOLOGICAL SEMINARY.   North Little
Rock, Little Rock, Arkansas 72101 U. S. A. (African
Methodist Church Episcopal).   1216
ST. JOHN'S HOME MISSIONS.   2500 North Tyler Street,
Little Rock, Arkansas   72207 U. S. A. (Roman Catho-
lic) 1911.   1217
NEW SUBIACO ABBEY.   Subiaco, Arkansas 72865
U. S. A. (Roman Catholic--Benedictines) 1878.
Library: 1930, 3, OB, OS, 25,000-15,000, DDC,
F-S, SC, 100-80, Ar Mi Ma Mu VF   1218

Arizona
CHRIST THE KING LIBRARY.   800 North Country Club
Road, Tucson, Arizona 85716 U. S. A.   (Roman Cath-
olic--Benedictine Sisters of Perpetual Adoration).
Library: 1950, 0, OS, 10,000-7,812, DDC, 47-9   1219
REGINA CLERI SEMINARY.   8800 East 22nd Street,
Tucson, Arizona 85710 U. S. A. (Roman Catholic).   1220

California
BERKELEY BAPTIST DIVINITY SCHOOL.   2606 Dwight
Way, Berkeley 4, California 94704 U. S. A. (American
Baptist Convention) 1871.
Sandford Fleming Library: 1871, 1, OB, OS,
75,000-60,000, E, UTS and LC, F-S, SC, 350-100,
Ar Mi Ma   1221
GRADUATE THEOLOGICAL UNION. 2465 LeConte
Avenue, Berkeley, California 94709 U. S. A. (Roman
Catholic--Dominican and Jesuit, Presbyterian, Ameri-
can Baptist, Lutheran, Unitarian, Methodist, Disciples,
United Church Groups) 1963.
Bibliographical Center: 1964, 5, OS, 10,000-3,500,
E, LC   1222
CHURCH DIVINITY SCHOOL OF THE PACIFIC.   2451
Ridge Road, Berkeley, California 94709. U. S. A.
(Protestant Episcopal Church) 1893.
James Otis Lincoln Library: 1893, 1, OB, OS,
50,000-29,862, E G, UTS and LC, SC, 190-150,
Mu   1223

PACIFIC LUTHERAN THEOLOGICAL SEMINARY.
2770 Marin Avenue, Berkeley, California 94797
U.S.A. (Lutheran Church in America) 1948.
Library: 1952, 1, OB, OS, 35,000-22,500, E, LC,
F-S, SC, 317-200, Ar Fi Sl Mi Pi Ma VF   1224
PACIFIC SCHOOL OF RELIGION. 1798 Scenic Avenue,
Berkeley, California 94709 U.S.A. (Interdenomina-
tional) 1866.
Charles Holbrook Library: 1866, 2, OB, OS,
200,000-133,000, E, LC, SC, Ar Mi Pi Ma VF   1225
PACIFIC SCHOOL OF RELIGION. 1798 Scenic Avenue,
Berkeley, California 94709 U.S.A. (Interdenomina-
tional) 1866.
Palestine Institute Library: 3,300 volumes   1226
ST. MARGARET'S HOUSE. 1820 Scenic Drive, Berke-
ley, California 94709 U.S.A. (Episcopal) 1950. 1227
STARR KING SCHOOL FOR THE MINISTRY. 2441
LeConte Avenue, Berkeley, California 94709 U.S.A.
(Independent) 1904.
Earl Morse Wilbur Library: 1904, 1, OB, OS,
26,000-23,600, E, LC, SC, 25-___, Ar Mi   1228
CLARETVILLE SEMINARY. 26812 West Mulholland
Highway, Calabasas, California 91302 U.S.A. (Roman
Catholic--Congregation of the Sons of the Immaculate
Heart of the Blessed Virgin Mary) 1950.
Library: 1950, 0, OB, OS, 9,000-5,000, E, DDC,
F-S, 20-5, Ar Sl   1229
ST. JOHN'S SEMINARY. 5012 East Seminary Road,
Camarillo, California 93010 U.S.A. (Roman Catholic)
1939.
Edward L. Doheny Memorial Library: 1939, 0, OB,
OS, 60,000-40,000, L, LC, F-S, SC, 200-150, Ar
Fi Sl Mi Pi Ma VF   1230
DISCIPLES SEMINARY FOUNDATION SCHOOL OF THE-
OLOGY. Foothill Boulevard at College Avenue, Clare-
mont, California 91711 U.S.A. (Disciples of Christ,
Methodist) 1956.   1231
CALIFORNIA BAPTIST THEOLOGICAL SEMINARY.
Seminary Knolls, Covina, California 91722 U.S.A.
(American Baptist Convention) 1944.
Library: 1946, 1+, OB, OS, 63,000-55,090, E F G,
DDC, 678-650, Ar Sl Mi Pi Ma Mu VF   1232
WESTERN BAPTIST BIBLE COLLEGE. 1800 Elm Street,
El Cerrito, California 94530 U.S.A. (General Associa-
tion of Regular Baptist Churches) 1946.
Library: 1946, 2, OB, OS, 26,000-18,000, E, DDC,
SC, 175-84, Ar Sl Pi Ma Mu VF   1233

California (cont.)
MENNONITE BRETHREN BIBLICAL SEMINARY.
4824 East Butter Avenue, Fresno, California 93700
U.S.A. (Mennonite Brethren Church of North Amer-
ica).   1234
MONTEREY-FRESNO DIOCESAN LIBRARY.   1530 North
Fresno Street, Box 1668, Fresno California 93717
U.S.A. (Roman Catholic) 1934.   1235
ST. PIUS X SEMINARY.   Twin Cities Road and Midway
Avenue, Galt, California 95632 U.S.A. (Roman Catho-
lic).   1236
TALBOT THEOLOGICAL SEMINARY.   13800 Biola Ave-
nue, La Mirada, California 90638 U.S.A. (Biola
Schools and Colleges, Inc.) 1952.
Biola Library: 1936, 3, OB, OS, 85,000-80,000,
E, DDC, F-S, SC, 637-425, Ar Sl Mi Pi Ma Mu
VF   1237
LOMA LINDA UNIVERSITY.   Loma Linda, California
92534 U.S.A. (Seventh Day Adventist) 1907.
Vernier-Radcliffe Memorial Library.   1238
BLOY HOUSE THEOLOGICAL TRAINING SCHOOL.   Los
Angeles, California 90018 U.S.A. (Episcopal).   1239
CALIFORNIA HOUSE OF ISRAEL.   5365 Wilshire
Boulevard, Los Angeles, California 90036 U.S.A.
(Jewish).   1240
JEWISH COMMUNITY LIBRARY.   590 North Vermont
Avenue, Los Angeles, California 90004 U.S.A. (Jew-
ish) 1947.   1241
HEBREW UNION COLLEGE--JEWISH INSTITUTE OF
RELIGION, CALIFORNIA SCHOOL.   8745 Appian Way,
Los Angeles, California 90046 U.S.A. (Union of
American Hebrew Congregations) 1958.
Library: 1958, 1, OS, 45,000-40,000, E Hebrew,
LC, 115-50, Mi Ma Mu VF   1242
SPANISH AMERICAN BAPTIST SEMINARY.   512 South
Indians Street, Los Angeles, California 90063 U.S.A.
(American Baptist Convention).   1243
ALMA COLLEGE.   P.O. Box 1258, Los Gatos, Cali-
fornia 95030 U.S.A. (Roman Catholic--Society of
Jesus) 1934.
Library: 1934, 3, OS, 100,000-66,000, E, LC,
450-450   1244
ST. PATRICK'S SEMINARY.   320 Middlefield Road,
Menlo Park, California 94025 U.S.A. (Roman Catho-
lic--Archdiocese of San Francisco) 1898.
Library: 1898, 1, OB, OS, 45,000-40,000, E, DDC
and LC, 250-50   1245

GOLDEN GATE BAPTIST THEOLOGICAL SEMINARY.
Mill Valley, California 94941 U.S.A. (Southern Bap-
tist Convention) 1944.
Library: 1944, 4, OB, OS, 75,000-64,258, E, UTS,
SC, 480-___, Ar Fi Sl Mi Pi Mu VF   1246
ST. ALBERT'S COLLEGE. 6172 Chabot Road, Oakland,
California 94618 U.S.A. (Roman Catholic--Dominican
Province of the Holy Name) 1932.
Library: 1932, 1, OB, OS, 100,000-___, E, DDC
and LC, F-S, SC, 240-100, Mi   1247
FULLER THEOLOGICAL SEMINARY. 135 North Oakland
Avenue, Pasadena, California 91101 U.S.A. (Independ-
ent) 1947.
McAlister Library: 1947, 3-1/2, OS, 225,000-
101,000, E, UTS and LC, 344-90, Ar Sl Mi Pi VF   1248
H. ORTON WILEY LIBRARY. 1539 East Howard Avenue,
Pasadena, California 91104 U.S.A. (Church of the
Nazarene).
Library: 1910, 2, OB, OS, 100,000-100,000, E,
DDC, 539-___, Ar Fi Sl Mi Pi Ma Mu VF   1249
SAN FRANCISCO THEOLOGICAL SEMINARY. San Ans-
elmo, California 94960 U.S.A. (United Presbyterian
Church in the U.S.A.) 1871.
Library: 1871, 2, OS, 200,000-140,000, E, UTS
and LC, SC, 450-200, Ar Mi VF   1250
IMMACULATE HEART SEMINARY. Alcala Park, San
Diego, California 92110 U.S.A. (Roman Catholic--
San Diego Diocese) 1947.   1251
UNIVERSITY OF SAN DIEGO--VERONA FATHERS
HOUSE OF STUDIES. San Diego, California 92110
U.S.A. (Roman Catholic--F.S.C.J.) 1961.   1252
FRANCISCAN THEOLOGICAL SEMINARY. Old Mission,
Santa Barbara, California 93105 U.S.A. (Roman
Catholic--Franciscan Friars) 1901.
Library: 1901, 12, OB, OS, 30,000-27,000, E,
DDC, SC, 200-105, Ar VF   1253

Colorado
CONSERVATIVE BAPTIST THEOLOGICAL SEMINARY.
1500 East Tenth Avenue, Denver, Colorado 80218
U.S.A. (Conservative Baptist Association) 1950.
Carey S. Thomas Library: 1950, 1, OB, OS,
35,000-27,100, E, LC, 340-250, Fi Sl Mi Pi Ma
VF   1254
ILIFF SCHOOL OF THEOLOGY. Denver, Colorado
80210 U.S.A. (Methodist) 1892.
Ira J. Taylor Library: 1892, 4, OB, OS, 130,000-

Colorado (cont.)
70,000, E, UTS, SC, 450-___, Ar Mi   1255
ST. ANDREW AVELLINO SEMINARY.   1050 South Birch
Street, Denver, Colorado 80222   U.S.A. (Roman
Catholic) 1955.   1256
ST. THOMAS THEOLOGICAL SEMINARY.   1300 South
Steele Street, Denver, Colorado 80210 U.S.A.
(Roman Catholic) 1906.   1257

Connecticut
HOLY APOSTLES SEMINARY.   33 Prospect Hill Road,
Cromwell, Connecticut 06416   U.S.A. (Roman Catho-
lic) 1956.   1258
HARTFORD SEMINARY FOUNDATION.   55 Elizabeth
Street, Hartford, Connecticut 06105 U.S.A. (Inter-
denominational) 1834.
Case Memorial Library: 1834, 5, OS, 200,000-
194,054, E, LC and own, SC, 1,000-484, Ar Sl   1259
ST. LOUIS DE MONTFORT.   Litchfield, Connecticut
06759 U.S.A. (Roman Catholic) 1947.   1260
HOLY PROTECTION MONASTERY.   82 Pomus Road,
New Canaan, Connecticut 06840 U.S.A. (Orthodox)
1949.   1261
BERKELEY DIVINITY SCHOOL.   140 Prospect Street,
New Haven, Connecticut 06511   U.S.A. (Protestant
Episcopal) 1854.   1262
NEW HAVEN DISCIPLES HOUSE AND CENTER.   New
Haven, Connecticut 06511 U.S.A. (Disciples of
Christ).   1263
YALE UNIVERSITY DIVINITY SCHOOL.   409 Prospect
Street, New Haven, Connecticut 06510 U.S.A. (Inde-
pendent) 1701.
Library: 1932, 15, OB, OS, 300,000-246,285, E,
UTS, SC, 842-555, Ar Sl Mi VF   1264
SAINT MARY'S SEMINARY.   Weed Avenue, Norwalk,
Connecticut 06850 U.S.A.   (Roman Catholic--Holy
Ghost Fathers) 1904.
Library: 1904, 1, OB, OS, 40,000-14,000, DDC,
80-40   1265

District of Columbia
ATONEMENT SEMINARY.   145 Taylor Street, N.E.,
Washington, D.C. 20017 U.S.A. (Roman Catholic)
1957.   1266
AUGUSTINIAN COLLEGE.   3900 Harewood Road, N.E.,
Washington, D.C. 20017 U.S.A. (Roman Catholic)
1920.   1267

CATHOLIC UNIVERSITY OF AMERICA.   Washington,
  D.C. 20017 U.S.A. (Roman Catholic) 1887.
  Library: 1887, 2, OS, 100,000-83,000, LC and
  Petersen, F-S, SC, 400-400, Ar Fi Sl Mi Ma
  Mu VF   1268
CLARETIAN HOUSE OF STUDIES.   700 Monroe Street,
  N.E., Washington, D.C. 20017 U.S.A. (Roman Catho-
  lic) 1958.   1269
CONSOLATA HOUSE OF STUDIES.   1325 Otis Street,
  N.E., Washington, D.C. 20017 U.S.A. (Roman Catho-
  lic) 1952.   1270
DOMINICAN HOUSE OF STUDIES.   487 Michigan Avenue,
  N.E., Washington, D.C. 20017 U.S.A. (Roman Catho-
  lic--Dominican Order) 1905.
  Library: 1905, 5, OB, OS, 55,000-38,000, E L,
  DDC, SC, 240-___ , Ar Sl Mi Pi VF   1271
FRANCISCAN MONASTERY.   1400 Quincy Street, N.E.,
  Washington, D.C. 20017 U.S.A. (Roman Catholic--
  Order of Friars Minor) 1898.
  Library: 1898, 2, OB, OS, 25,000-20,000, DDC,
  F-S, SC, 50-35, Ar Pi Ma VF   1272
HOLY CROSS COLLEGE.   4001 Harewood Road, N.E.,
  Washington, D.C. 20017 U.S.A. (Roman Catholic--
  Congregation of Holy Cross) 1897.
  Library: 1897, 0, OB, OS, 40,000-35,000, E, LC
  and Petersen, F-S, SC, 204-154, Fi Sl Pi Ma Mu
  VF   1273
HOLY CROSS MISSIONS.   4301 Harewood Road, N.E.,
  Washington, D.C. 20017 U.S.A. (Roman Catholic--
  Holy Cross Missionary Society) 1924.
  Library: 1924, 2, OB, OS, 5,000-3,500, E, LC
  and Petersen, F-S, 24-0, Fi Sl   1274
HOLY NAME COLLEGE.   14th and Shepherd Streets,
  N.E., Washington, D.C. 20017 U.S.A. (Roman Cath-
  olic--Order of Friars Minor) 1930.
  Library: 1930, 1, OB, OS, 35,000-35,000, E,
  DDC, SC, 210-200   1275
HOWARD UNIVERSITY--SCHOOL OF RELIGION.
  Washington, D.C. 20001 U.S.A. (Non-denominational)
  1867.
  Library: 1940, 1, OS, 70,000-57,000, DDC and
  Auburn Seminary, 204-150, Fi Sl Mi Pi Mu VF   1276
IMMACULATE HEART SEMINARY.   721 Lawrence
  Street, N.E., Washington, D.C. 20017 U.S.A. (Roman
  Catholic) 1956.   1277
MARIAN FATHERS SEMINARY.   3885 Harewood Road,
  N.E., Washington, D.C. 20017 U.S.A. (Roman

District of Columbia (cont.)
Catholic) 1931.   1278
MARIST COLLEGE. 3875 Harewood Road, N.E., Wash-
ington, D.C. 20017 U.S.A. (Roman Catholic--Society
of Mary) 1892.
Library: 1892, 6, OB, OS, 25,000-25,000, E F L,
LC, F-S, SC, 150-75, VF   1279
OBLATE COLLEGE. 391 Michigan Avenue, Washington,
D.C. 20017 U.S.A. (Roman Catholic--Missionary Ob-
lates of Mary Immaculate) 1917.
Library: 1917, 3, OB, OS, 35,000-21,142, DDC, F-S,
SC, 231-   1280
ORATORY OF ST. PHILIP NERI. 3514 Fifteenth
Street, N.E., Washington, D.C. 20017 U.S.A. (Roman
Catholic) 1955.   1281
OUR LADY OF LEBANON MARONITE SEMINARY. 7164
Alaska Avenue, N.W., Washington, D.C. 20012 U.S.A.
(Roman Catholic--Maronite Rite) 1961.   1282
QUEEN OF PIOUS SCHOOLS COLLEGE. 1339 Monroe
Street, N.E., Washington, D.C. 20017 U.S.A. (Roman
Catholic) 1954.   1283
QUEEN OF THE APOSTLES SEMINARY. 4000 Thir-
teenth Street, N.E., Washington, D.C. 20017 U.S.A.
(Roman Catholic) 1939.   1284
ST. FRANCIS CAPUCHIN COLLEGE. 4121 Harewood
Road, N.E., Washington, D.C. 20017 U.S.A. (Roman
Catholic) 1918.   1285
ST. JOSEPH SEMINARY. 1200 Varnum Street, N.E.,
Washington, D.C. 20017 U.S.A. (Roman Catholic--
Society of Jesus) 1888.   1286
ST. JOSEPH'S UKRANIAN SEMINARY. 201 Taylor
Street, N.E., Washington, D.C. 20017 U.S.A. (Roman
Catholic--Byzantine Ukranian Rite) 1941.   1287
ST. PAUL'S COLLEGE. 3015 Fourth Street, N.E.,
Washington, D.C. 20017 U.S.A. (Roman Catholic--
Paulist Fathers) 1889.
Library: 1889, 1, OB, OS, 60,000-38,000, E,
DDC, F-S, SC, 387-291, Ar Sl Mi Pi Ma Mu VF   1288
ST. THOMAS MORE HOUSE OF STUDIES. Washington,
D.C. U.S.A. (Roman Catholic) 1941.   1289
STIGMATINE FATHERS HOUSE OF STUDIES. 1326
Quincy Street, N.E., Washington, D.C. 20017 U.S.A.
(Roman Catholic--Stigmatine Fathers) 1956.
Library: 1956, 3, OB, OS, 5,000-3,000, E, LC
and Cutter, F-S, SC, 52-43, Ar Pi Ma   1290
THEOLOGICAL COLLEGE. 401 Michigan Avenue, N.E.,
Washington, D.C. 20017 U.S.A. (Roman Catholic)

1918.
Library: 1918, 22, OB, OS, 35,000-30,000, E,
DDC, F-S, SC, 150-100, Ar Mu   1291
THEOLOGICAL COLLEGE OF OUR LADY OF MT.
CARMEL. 2132 Lincoln Road, N. E. , Washington,
D. C. 20002 U. S. A. (Roman Catholic) 1916.   1292
VIATORIAN SEMINARY. 1212 Otis Street, N. E. ,
Washington, D. C. 20017 U. S. A. (Roman Catholic)
1961.   1293
WESLEY THEOLOGICAL SEMINARY. 4400 Massachu-
setts Avenue, N.W. , Washington, D.C. 20016 U.S. A.
(Methodist) 1890.
Library: 1890, 6, OB, OS, 100,000-60,000, E F G,
DDC, 475-400, Ar Sl Mi   1294
WHITE FRIARS HALL. 1600 Webster Street, N. E. ,
Washington, D. C. 20017 U. S. A. (Roman Catholic--
Carmelite Fathers) 1939.
Library: 1939, 1, OB, OS, 15,000-10,000, E F G,
LC and Petersen, F-S, 150-100, Mi VF   1295

Florida
SEMINARY OF ST. VINCENT DE PAUL. P. O. Box 460,
Boynton Beach, Florida 33435 U. S. A. (Roman Catholic
--Congregation of the Mission) 1963.
Library: 1962, 0, OB, OS, 40,000-14,000, E, LC,
SC, 150-63, Mi Ma   1296
THREE HIERARCHS SEMINARY. P. O. Box 65, Mait-
land, Florida 32751 U. S. A. (Eastern Orthodox Catho-
lic Church in America, Inc.) 1965.
Library: 1965, 1, OB, OS, ___-400, E, LC, SC,
25-0, Sl   1297
ST. LEO ABBEY. St. Leo, Florida 33574 U.S.A.
(Roman Catholic).   1298

Georgia
BEULAH HEIGHTS COLLEGE. 892-906 Berne Street,
S. E. , Atlanta, Georgia 30316 U. S. A. (Independent)
1928.
Barth Memorial Library: 1928, 1, OB, OS, 15,000-
6,000, 25-___ , Mu VF   1299
EMORY UNIVERSITY. Atlanta, Georgia 30322 U. S. A.
(Methodist) 1914.
Theology Library: 1914, 8, OS, 150,000-80,000
E G, LC, F-S, SC, 354-___ , Fi Mi   1300
INTERDENOMINATIONAL THEOLOGICAL CENTER.
671 Beckwith Street, S. W. , Atlanta, Georgia 30314
U. S. A. (Interdenominational) 1958.   1301

Georgia (cont.)
PHILLIP SCHOOL OF THEOLOGY. Atlanta, Georgia
30314, U. S. A. (Christian Methodist Episcopal).   1302
COLUMBIA THEOLOGICAL SEMINARY. Decatur,
Georgia 30031 U. S. A. (Presbyterian Church--U. S.)
1828.
John Bulow Campbell Library: 1828, 2, OB, OS,
100,000-75,000, E, UTS, SC, 191-__, Mi   1303

Illinois
AURORA COLLEGE--THEOLOGICAL DEPARTMENT.
347 Gladstone, Aurora, Illinois 60507 U. S. A.
(Seventh Day Adventist) 1893.   1304
MARMION ABBEY. Butterfield Road, Aurora, Illinois
60504 U. S. A. (Roman Catholic--Benedictine Com-
munity of St. Augustine) 1947.
Library: 1947, 2, OB, OS, 12,000-10,000, E, DDC,
F-S, 77-70, Ma VF   1305
CHICAGO THEOLOGICAL SEMINARY. 5757 University
Avenue, Chicago, Illinois 60637 U. S. A. (United Church
of Christ) 1882.   1306
COLLEGE OF JEWISH STUDIES. 72 East 11th Street,
Chicago, Illinois 60605 U. S. A. (Board of Jewish
Education) 1925.
Leaf Library: 1930, 4, OB, 50,000-40,000, Hebrew,
Freidus, 200-195   1307
DISCIPLES DIVINITY HOUSE. 1156 East 57th Street,
Chicago, Illinois 60637 U. S. A. (Disciples of Christ).   1308
HEBREW THEOLOGICAL COLLEGE. 3448 Douglas
Boulevard, Chicago, Illinois 60623 U. S. A. (Jewish)
1922.   1309
LUTHERAN SCHOOL OF THEOLOGY AT CHICAGO.
1100 East 55th Street, Chicago, Illinois 60615 U. S. A.
(Lutheran Church in America) 1962.
Library: 1962, 3, OS, 130,000-90,000, Danish E
Finnish G Swedish, LC, SC, 677-450, Ar Fi Sl Mi
Ma Mu VF   1310
McCORMICK THEOLOGICAL SEMINARY. 800 West
Belden Avenue, Chicago, Illinois 60614 U. S. A. (United
Presbyterian Church in the U. S. A.) 1829.
McGaw Memorial Library: 1829, 5, OS, 400,000-
144,000, LC, SC, 550-375, Ar Sl Mi   1311
MEADVILLE THEOLOGICAL SCHOOL. 5701 Woodlawn
Avenue, Chicago, Illinois 60637 U. S. A. (Unitarian
Universalist) 1844.
Library: 1844, 2, OB, 90,000-72,000, E, LC,
120-100, Ar Pi Mu VF   1312

MOODY BIBLE INSTITUTE. 820 North LaSalle Street, Chicago, Illinois 60610 U.S.A. (Non-denominational) 1888.
Library: 1890, 4, OB, OS, 72,000-65,000, E, DDC, F-S, SC, 461-180, Mi Ma Mu VF   1313

NORTH PARK THEOLOGICAL SEMINARY. 5125 North Spaulding Avenue, Chicago, Illinois 60625 U.S.A. (Evangelical Covenant Church of America) 1891.
Mellander Library: 1891, 2, OS, 75,000-30,200, E, DDC, SC, 275-203, Ar Mi Ma VF   1314

UNIVERSITY OF CHICAGO DIVINITY SCHOOL. 5801 South Ellis Avenue, Chicago, Illinois 60637 U.S.A. (Baptist Theological Union) 1890.
Swift Library (Library for Divinity and Philosophy): 1890, 7, OB, OS, 150,000-152,000, E, LC, F-S, 500-500, Ar Fi Sl Mi Pi Ma Mu VF   1315

TRINITY EVANGELICAL DIVINITY SCHOOL. 2045 Half Day Road, Bannockburn, Deerfield, Illinois 60015 U.S.A. (Evangelical Free Churches of America) 1897.
Library: 1897, 4, OB, OS, 30,000-17,000, E, Bliss and UTS, F-S, 280-0, Ar   1316

GARRETT THEOLOGICAL SEMINARY. 2121 Sheridan Road, Evanston, Illinois 60201 U.S.A. (Methodist) 1855.
Library: 1855, 6, OB, OS, 175,000-175,000, E, LC, SC, 560-___, Ar Fi Sl Mi Pi Ma Mu VF   1317

SEABURY-WESTERN THEOLOGICAL SEMINARY. 2122 Sheridan Road, Evanston, Illinois 60201 U.S.A. (Protestant Episcopal Church in the U.S.A.) 1858.
Library: 1858, 1, OB, OS, 65,000-59,780, E, LC, SC, 260-235, Fi Sl Mi   1318

STONEBRIDGE PRIORY. Lake Bluff, Illinois 60004 U.S.A. (Roman Catholic) 1945.   1319

ST. MARY OF THE LAKE SEMINARY. Mundelein, Illinois 60060 U.S.A. (Roman Catholic) 1921.
Feehan Memorial Library: 1925, 1, OB, OS, 120,000-123,347, E F G I, LC, F-S, SC, 355-___, Ar Fi Sl Mi Pi Ma VF   1320

EVANGELICAL THEOLOGICAL SEMINARY. 329 East School Avenue, Naperville, Illinois 60540 U.S.A. (Evangelical United Brethren Church) 1873.
College and Seminary Library (Seminary Collection): 1873, 6, OB, OS, 50,000-29,957, E, DDC, SC, 206-119, Ar Fi Sl Mi VF   1321

BELLARMINE SCHOOL OF THEOLOGY. 230 South Lincoln Way, North Aurora, Illinois 60542 U.S.A.

Illinois (cont.)
(Roman Catholic--Society of Jesus) 1934.
Library: 1934, 2, OS, 150,000-107,495, E L,
DDC, F-S, 442-401   1322
BETHANY THEOLOGICAL SEMINARY. Butterfield
Road and Meyers Road, Oak Brook, Illinois 60523
U.S.A. (Church of the Brethren) 1905.   1323
NORTHERN BAPTIST THEOLOGICAL SEMINARY. Oak
Brook, Illinois 60521 U.S.A. (American Baptist Con-
vention) 1913.
A. H. Karpe Library: 1913, 3, OB, OS, 100,000-
62,400, DDC, 314-150, Ar Sl Pi Ma VF   1324
TOLENTINE COLLEGE. Box 747, Olympia Fields, Illi-
nois 60461 U.S.A. (Roman Catholic--Order of St.
Augustine) 1958.
Library: 1958, 1-1/2, OB, OS, 25,000-13,000, E,
LC, 135-10, Mi VF   1325
OUR LADY OF ANGELS SEMINARY. 1901 North 18th
Street, Quincy, Illinois 62301 U.S.A. (Roman Catho-
lic--Order of Friars Minor) 1859.
Library: 1859, 1, OB, OS, 75,000-32,000, E, DDC,
SC, 115-54, Ar Sl Ma Mu   1326
AQUINAS INSTITUTE OF PHILOSOPHY AND THEOLOGY.
7200 West Division Street, River Forest, Illinois
62639 U.S.A. (Roman Catholic) 1925.   1327
HEBREW THEOLOGICAL COLLEGE. 7135 Carpenter
Road, Skokie, Illinois 60076 U.S.A. (Hebrew Theo-
logical College--Beth Midrash L' Torah) 1922.
Saul Silber Memorial Library: 1922, 3, OB,
___-45,000, Hebrew, Freidus, F-S, SC, 85-15, Ar
Mi Mu VF   1328
CONCORDIA THEOLOGICAL SEMINARY. Springfield,
Illinois 62702 U.S.A. (Lutheran Church--Missouri
Synod) 1846.
Schulz Memorial Library: 1875, 3, OS, 200,000-
48,538, E, LC, SC, 475-180, Fi Sl Mi Pi Ma VF   1329
DIVINE WORD SEMINARY. Techny, Illinois 60082
U.S.A. (Roman Catholic) 1909.   1330
ST. JOSEPH SEMINARY. Teutopolis, Illinois 62467
U.S.A. (Roman Catholic--Franciscan Fathers of the
Sacred Heart Province) 1862.
Library: 1862, 0, OB, OS, 37,000-34,500, E,
DDC, SC, 290-250   1331
CHRIST THE KING SEMINARY. P.O. Box 246, West
Chicago, Illinois 60185 U.S.A. (Roman Catholic)
1955.   1332

Indiana
ANDERSON COLLEGE--SCHOOL OF THEOLOGY. Ander-
    son, Indiana 46012 U.S.A. (Church of God: Ander-
    son, Indiana) 1950.
    Library: 1950, 1, OB, OS, 50,000-29,000, UTS,
    SC, 236-60, Sl Mi VF   1333
CAPUCHIN SEMINARY OF ST. MARY. Route 2, Box
    185, Crown Point, Indiana 46307 U.S.A. (Roman
    Catholic) 1959.   1334
MENNONITE BIBLICAL SEMINARY. 3003 Benham Ave-
    nue, Elkhart, Indiana 46514 U.S.A. (General Confer-
    ence Mennonite Church) 1948.
    Library: 1921, 1, OB, OS, 35,000-33,000, E G,
    DDC, 268-172, Sl Mi Ma VF   1335
CROZER HOUSE OF STUDIES. 2620 East Wallen Road,
    Fort Wayne, Indiana 46805 U.S.A. (Roman Catholic)
    1932.   1336
GOSHEN COLLEGE BIBLICAL SEMINARY. Goshen,
    Indiana 46526 U.S.A. (Mennonite Church) 1903.
    Library: 1958, 2, OB, OS, 50,000-36,330, E G,
    DDC, SC, 400-   , Ar Fi Sl Mi Pi Ma Mu VF   1337
HUNTINGTON COLLEGE. Huntington, Indiana 46750
    U.S.A. (United Brethren in Christ) 1897.
    Loew-Alumni Library: 1897, 2, OS, 60,000-5,866,
    DDC, 35-7, Sl Mi Ma   1338
CATHOLIC SEMINARY OF INDIANAPOLIS. 4615 North
    Michigan Road, Indianapolis, Indiana 46208 U.S.A.
    (Roman Catholic--Order of St. Benedict) 1967.
    Library: 24,500 volumes   1339
CENTRAL BAPTIST THEOLOGICAL SEMINARY OF
    INDIANA. 1519-41 Martindale Avenue, Indianapolis,
    Indiana 46202 U.S.A. (Northern Baptist U.S.A.,
    Northern Baptist of America, Progressive Baptists). 1340
CHRISTIAN THEOLOGICAL SEMINARY. 1000 West
    42nd Street, Box 88267, Indianapolis, Indiana 46208
    U.S.A. (Disciples of Christ) 1942.
    Library: 1924, 4, OB, OS, 85,000-70,300, E, DDC,
    530-   , Fi Sl Mi Pi Ma Mu VF   1341
EARLHAM SCHOOL OF RELIGION. College Avenue,
    Richmond, Indiana 47374 U.S.A. (Society of Friends)
    1847.   1342
ARCHABBEY LIBRARY. St. Meinrad, Indiana 47577
    U.S.A. (Roman Catholic--Order of St. Benedict).
    Library: 1854, 3, OB, OS, 80,000-70,000, E G L
    Romance, LC, SC, 490-193, Mi Pi Ma VF   1343
HOLY CROSS HALL. St. Meinrad, Indiana 47577 U.S.A.
    (Roman Catholic--Passionist Fathers) 1905.

Indiana (cont.)
Passionist Theological Library: 1905, 5, OB, OS,
30,000-25,000, E, DDC, F-S, SC, 212-85, VF   1344
UNION BIBLE SEMINARY. 434 South Union Street,
Westfield, Indiana 46074 U.S.A. (Independent) 1911.
McFarland Library: 1911, 0, OS, 1,000-1,000, E,
DDC, F-S, 0-0   1345

Iowa
DRAKE UNIVERSITY DIVINITY SCHOOL. Des Moines,
Iowa 50311 U.S.A. (Disciples of Christ) 1897.
Library: 2, OS, 25,000-29,000, DDC, 300-__, Ar
Mi Pi Ma VF   1346
AQUINAS INSTITUTE SCHOOL OF THEOLOGY. St.
Rose Priory, 2570 Asbury, Dubuque, Iowa 52001
U.S.A. (Roman Catholic--Order of Friars Preachers)
1956.
Agnes S. Cunningham Memorial Library: 1956, 2,
OS, 80,000-33,303, E L, DDC and Petersen, SC, 324-
324, Fi Mi VF   1347
DUBUQUE THEOLOGICAL SEMINARY. 2050 University
Avenue, Dubuque, Iowa 52002 U.S.A. (United Presby-
terian Church in the U.S.A.) 1852.   1348
MT. ST. BERNARD SEMINARY. Carter Road, Dubuque,
Iowa 52001 U.S.A. (Roman Catholic) 1953.
Library: 1953, 1, OB, OS, 30,000-21,000, E, DDC,
F-S, 220-200, Fi Mi   1349
NEW MELLERAY ABBEY. Dubuque, Iowa 52001 U.S.A.
(Roman Catholic--Order of Cistercians of the Strict
Observance) 1849.
Library: 1849, 1, OB, OS, 15,000-8,000, E, DDC,
F-S, 50-__, Ar   1350
WARTBURG SEMINARY. Dubuque, Iowa 52001 U.S.A.
(American Lutheran Church) 1854.
Reu Memorial Library: 1854, 1, OS, __-65,000,
E, UTS, 215-179, Sl   1351
DIVINE WORD SEMINARY. Epworth, Iowa 52045 U.S.A.
(Roman Catholic--Society of Divine Word) 1963.
Library: 1963, 3, OB, OS, 50,000-28,000, E, DDC,
F-S, 215-150, Sl Mi Ma Mu VF   1352

Kansas
CENTRAL BAPTIST THEOLOGICAL SEMINARY. 2915
Minnesota Avenue, Kansas City, Kansas 66102 U.S.A.
(American Baptist Convention) 1901.
Library: 1901, 1, OB, OS, 120,000-52,000, E,
DDC, 335-250, Ar Fi Sl Mi Pi Ma Mu VF   1353

ST. MARY'S COLLEGE. Kansas City, Kansas 66536
U.S.A. (Roman Catholic--Society of Jesus) 1931.   1354

Kentucky
EPISCOPAL THEOLOGICAL SEMINARY IN KENTUCKY.
Lexington, Kentucky 40508 U.S.A. (Episcopal).   1355
LEXINGTON THEOLOGICAL SEMINARY. South Lime-
stone, Lexington, Kentucky 40508 U.S.A. (Disciples
of Christ) 1865.
Library: 1865, 2, OB, OS, 75,000-60,000, UTS,
F-S, 900-___, Ar Fi Sl Mi Pi Ma VF   1356
LOUISVILLE PRESBYTERIAN THEOLOGICAL SEMINARY.
1044 Alta Vista Road, Louisville, Kentucky 40205
U.S.A. (Presbyterian Church in the U.S., United Pres-
byterian Church in the U.S.A.) 1853.
Library: 1853, 3, OB, OS, 100,000-44,182, E, UTS,
SC, 173-150, Ar Mi   1357
SIMMONS UNIVERSITY. 1811 Dumesnil Street, Louis-
ville, Kentucky 40210 U.S.A. (Baptist General Associ-
ation of Kentucky) 1873.
Library: 1873, 1, OB, 7,626-3,813, DDC, 40-___,
Fi Sl Pi Ma Mu   1358
SOUTHERN BAPTIST THEOLOGICAL SEMINARY. 2825
Lexington Road, Louisville, Kentucky 40206 U.S.A.
(Southern Baptist Convention) 1859.
James P. Boyce Library: 1859, 6, OB, OS, 350,000-
138,000, E, DDC, SC, 1,114-639, Ar Fi Sl Mi Ma
Mu VF   1359
OUR LADY OF GETHSEMANE. Trappist, Kentucky
40073 U.S.A. (Roman Catholic) 1848.   1360
ST. MAUR'S SEMINARY. South Union, Kentucky 42283
U.S.A. (Roman Catholic--Order of St. Benedict)
1954.
Library: 1955, 1, OS, 40,000-24,000, E G L, DDC,
SC, 150-0, Ar Sl Mi Ma Mu VF   1361
ASBURY THEOLOGICAL SEMINARY. Wilmore, Kentucky
40390 U.S.A. (Interdenominational) 1923.
B. L. Fisher Library: 1939, 4, OB, OS, 150,000-
61,000, E, UTS, 560-___, Sl Mi VF   1362

Louisiana
ST. JOSEPH CATHEDRAL PREPARATORY SEMINARY.
421 North Street, Baton Rouge, Louisiana 70801
U.S.A. (Roman Catholic) 1964.   1363
NEW ORLEANS BAPTIST THEOLOGICAL SEMINARY.
4110 Seminary Place, New Orleans, Louisiana 70126
U.S.A. (Southern Baptist Convention) 1917.

Louisiana (cont.)

Library: 1917, 3, OB, OS, 125,000-112,000, E,
DDC, F-S, SC, 700-500, Sl Mi Mu   1364
NOTRE DAME SEMINARY.   2901 South Carrollton Ave-
nue, New Orleans, Louisiana 70118 U.S.A. (Roman
Catholic) 1923.

Library: 1923, 1, OB, OS, 200,000-42,895, E F I L,
DDC, F-S, SC, 110-___, Ar Fi Sl Mi Ma   1365

Maine

BANGOR THEOLOGICAL SEMINARY.   Bangor, Maine
04401 U.S.A. (United Church of Christ) 1959.   1366

Maryland

NER ISRAEL RABBINICAL COLLEGE.   4411 Garrison
Boulevard, Baltimore, Maryland 21215 U.S.A. (Jew-
ish).   1367
ST. MARY'S SEMINARY AND UNIVERSITY.   5400 Roland
Avenue, Roland Park, Baltimore, Maryland 21210
U.S.A. (Roman Catholic--Fathers of the Society of
St. Sulpice) 1891.

Library: 1891, 1, OS, 100,000-85,000, E F G,
DDC, SC, 285-210, Ar Sl Mi Pi Ma VF   1368
TALMUDICAL ACADEMY OF BALTIMORE.   3701 Cot-
tage Avenue, Baltimore, Maryland 21215 U.S.A.
(Jewish) 1947.   1369
TRINITARIAN COLLEGE.   Box 5742, Baltimore, Mary-
land 21208 U.S.A. (Roman Catholic--Order of the
Most Holy Trinity) 1958.

Library: 1958, 2, OS, 20,000-12,000, E, LC, 150-
___, Sl Mi Ma Mu VF   1370
MT. ST. MARY'S SEMINARY.   Emmitsburg, Maryland
21727 U.S.A. (Roman Catholic) 1808.   1371
OBLATES OF ST. FRANCES DE SALES.   Hyattsville,
Maryland 20781 U.S.A. (Roman Catholic) 1924.   1372
DIVINE SAVIOR SEMINARY.   Lanham, Maryland 20801
U.S.A. (Roman Catholic--Society of the Divine Savior)
1926.

Library: 1941, 4, OB, OS, 50,000-18,000, E, LC,
125-90, Mi Ma Mu VF   1373
HOLY FAMILY SEMINARY.   1401 Randolph Road, Silver
Spring, Maryland 20902 U.S.A. (Roman Catholic)
1946.   1374
HOLY TRINITY MISSIONS SEMINARY.   9001 New Hamp-
shire Avenue, Silver Spring, Maryland 20910 U.S.A.
(Roman Catholic) 1954.   1375
PALLOTTI COLLEGE.   2009 Van Buren Street, West

Hyattsville, Maryland 20782 U.S.A. (Roman Catholic)
1950.   1376
WOODSTOCK COLLEGE. Woodstock, Maryland 21163
U.S.A. (Roman Catholic--Society of Jesus) 1868.   1377

Massachusetts
ST. FRANCIS SERAPHIC SEMINARY. Andover, Massa-
chusetts 01810 U.S.A. (Roman Catholic) 1930.   1378
BOSTON UNIVERSITY SCHOOL OF THEOLOGY. 745
Commonwealth Avenue, Boston, Massachusetts 02215
U.S.A. (Methodist Episcopal Church) 1839.
Library: 1839, 5, OB, OS, 100,000-78,665, E, DDC,
F-S, SC, 650-500, Ar Mi Mu VF   1379
CONGREGATIONAL LIBRARY. 14 Beacon Street, Boston,
Massachusetts 02108 U.S.A. (American Congregational
Association).
Library: 1853, 8, OS, 250,000-200,000, E, own, SC,
125-   , Ar Mi   1380
MASSACHUSETTS NEW-CHURCH UNION. 3 Joy Street,
Boston, Massachusetts 02108 U.S.A. (Swedenborgian)
1964.
Library: 1854, 0, OS, 6,000-6,000, E, 10-0   1381
ST. JOHN'S SEMINARY. Lake Street, Brighton, Massa-
chusetts 02135 U.S.A. (Roman Catholic Archbishop
of Boston) 1884.
Library: 1884, 2, OB, OS, 250,000-777,200, LC,
F-S, 225-200, Mi   1382
HOLY CROSS GREEK ORTHODOX THEOLOGICAL SEMI-
NARY. 50 Goddard Avenue, Brookline, Massachu-
setts 02146 U.S.A. (Greek Orthodox) 1954.   1383
EPISCOPAL THEOLOGICAL SCHOOL. 99 Brattle Street,
Cambridge, Massachusetts 02138 U.S.A. (Episcopal)
1867.   1384
HARVARD DIVINITY SCHOOL. 45 Francis Avenue,
Cambridge, Massachusetts 02138 U.S.A. (Non-de-
nominational) 1815.
Andover-Harvard Theological Library: 1910, 8, OB,
OS, 325,000-280,000, multi-lingual, Cutter, SC,
1,200-1,100, Ar Mi VF   1385
LA SALETTE SEMINARY. Ipswich, Massachusetts
01938 U.S.A. (Roman Catholic--Missionaries of Our
Lady of La Salette) 1924.
Library: 1955, 3, OB, OS, 15,000-15,000, E, DDC,
F-S, SC, 85-50, VF   1386
BERKSHIRE CHRISTIAN COLLEGE. 200 Stockbridge
Road, Lenox, Massachusetts 01240 U.S.A. (Advent
Christian Church) 1897.

Massachusetts (cont.)

Linden J. Carter Library: 1952, 1, OS, 20,000-
16,000, E, DDC, 238-108, Ar Sl Mi Ma Mu VF   1387
CRANE THEOLOGICAL SCHOOL OF TUFTS UNIVER-
SITY. Medford, Massachusetts 02155 U.S.A. (Uni-
tarian, Universalist) 1852.   1388
ST. BASIL'S SEMINARY. East and Pleasant Streets,
Methuen, Massachusetts 01844 U.S.A. (Roman Cath-
olic) 1953.   1389
ST. COLOMBAN'S MAJOR SEMINARY. 1200 Brush Hill
Road, Milton, Massachusetts 02186 U.S.A. (Roman
Catholic) 1953.   1390
OBLATE COLLEGE AND SEMINARY. 109 Woodland
Street, Natick, Massachusetts 01760 U.S.A. (Roman
Catholic--Oblates of Mary Immaculate) 1927.
Library: 1927, 1, OB, OS, 40,000-25,000, E F L,
DDC, F-S, 200-150, Ar   1391
NEW CHURCH THEOLOGICAL SCHOOL. 48 Sargent
Street, Newton, Massachusetts 02158 U.S.A. (Sweden-
borgian) 1866.   1392
ANDOVER NEWTON THEOLOGICAL SCHOOL. 169 Her-
rick Road, Newton Centre, Massachusetts 02159
U.S.A. (American Baptist Convention, United Church
of Christ) 1807.
Hills Library: 1807, 2, OB, OS, 75,000-95,000, E,
Cutter, SC, 400-300, Ar Mi VF   1393
ST. JOSEPH'S ABBEY. Spencer, Massachusetts 01562
U.S.A. (Roman Catholic) 1950.   1394
OUR LADY OF SORROWS MONASTERY. 96 Monastery
Avenue, P.O. Box 150, Springfield, Massachusetts
01107 U.S.A. (Roman Catholic) 1924.   1395
GORDON DIVINITY SCHOOL. 255 Grapevine Road, Wen-
ham, Massachusetts 01984 U.S.A. (Independent) 1889.
Library: 1945, 3-1/2, OS, 40,000-35,000, E, LC,
SC, 213-190, Mi VF   1396
POPE JOHN XXIII NATIONAL SEMINARY. Weston,
Massachusetts 02193 U.S.A. (Roman Catholic) 1964.   1397
WESTON COLLEGE. Weston, Massachusetts 02193
U.S.A. (Roman Catholic--Society of Jesus) 1921.
Library: 1922, 2, OB, OS, 100,000-110,000, E F
G L S, DDC, 450-___, Mi   1398

Michigan

ANDREWS UNIVERSITY. Berrien Springs, Michigan
49104 U.S.A. (Seventh-Day Adventist) 1935.
James White Library: 1937, 6-3/4, OB, OS,
280,000-165,000, E, LC, 1,582-___, Mi VF   1399

CALVIN THEOLOGICAL SEMINARY. 3233 Burton Street,
S.E., Grand Rapids, Michigan 49506 U.S.A. (Christian
Reformed Church) 1876. 1400
WESTERN THEOLOGICAL SEMINARY. 86 East 12th
Street, Holland, Michigan 49423 U.S.A. (Reformed
Church in America) 1866.
Beardslee Library: 1895, 1, OB, OS, 75,000-
46,600, D E G, DDC, 280-___, Ar Sl Mi Mu 1401
SS. CYRIL AND METHODIUS SEMINARY. Orchard
Lake, Michigan 48034 U.S.A. (Roman Catholic)
1885. 1402
SAINT JOHN'S SEMINARY LIBRARY. 44011 Five
Mile Road, P.O. Box 298, Plymouth, Michigan
48170 U.S.A. (Roman Catholic--Society of St. Sul-
pice) 1949.
Library: 1949, 1, OB, OS, 88,200-21,000, E, LC,
SC, 230-200, Ar Fi Sl Mi Ma 1403
ST. PAUL OF THE CROSS SCHOLASTICATE. 23300
Davison, West Detroit, Michigan 48223 U.S.A. (Roman
Catholic) 1932. 1404

Minnesota
ASSUMPTION SEMINARY AND COLLEGE. Chaska,
Minnesota 55318 U.S.A. (Roman Catholic) 1952. 1405
ST. JOHN'S UNIVERSITY. Collegeville, Minnesota
56321 U.S.A. (Roman Catholic--Order of St. Bene-
dict) 1857.
Library: 1875, 8-1/2, OB, OS, 450,000-160,000,
E G L, DDC and Petersen, SC, 1,080-___, Ar Mi
Ma VF 1406
LUTHERAN BIBLE SCHOOL AND SEMINARY. Fergus
Falls, Minnesota 56537 U.S.A. (Church of the Luth-
eran Brethren of America). 1407
BETHANY LUTHERAN SEMINARY. 734 Marsh Street,
Mankato, Minnesota 56011 U.S.A. (Evangelical Luth-
eran Synod) 1931. 1408
CENTRAL BAPTIST CONSERVATIVE SEMINARY. Min-
neapolis, Minnesota 55440 U.S.A. (Conservative Bap-
tist Association). 1409
UNITED THEOLOGICAL SEMINARY OF THE TWIN
CITIES. 3000 Fifth Street, N.W., New Brighton,
Minnesota 55112 U.S.A. (United Church of Christ)
1962.
Library: 1962, 1, OS, 100,000-27,000, E, UTS,
210-___, Fi Sl Mi 1410
BETHEL THEOLOGICAL SEMINARY. 3801 North Ham-
line Avenue, St. Paul, Minnesota 55112 U.S.A. (Bap-

Minnesota (cont.)
tist General Conference) 1871.
Library: 1871, 3, OB, OS, 75,000-25,000, E,
DDC, 510-254, Ar Sl Mi VF   1411
LUTHER THEOLOGICAL SEMINARY.   2375 Como Ave-
nue West, St. Paul, Minnesota 55108 U.S.A. (Ameri-
can Lutheran Church) 1869.
Library: 3, OS, 150,000-85,000, E G Scandinavian,
LC, 442-148, Ar Sl Mi Pi VF   1412
NORTHWESTERN LUTHERAN THEOLOGICAL SEMINARY.
1501 Fulham Street, St. Paul, Minnesota 55108 U.S.A.
(Lutheran Church in America) 1920.
Library: 1920, 1, OB, OS, 90,000-39,967, E, LC,
SC, 850-___, Ar Fi Mi Pi Ma Mu VF   1413
ST. PAUL SEMINARY.   2200 Grand Avenue, St. Paul,
Minnesota 55101 U.S.A. (Roman Catholic) 1894.   1414

Mississippi
DIVINE WORD SEMINARY OF ST. AUGUSTINE.   Bay St.
Louis, Mississippi 38520 U.S.A. (Roman Catholic)
1920.   1415
OUR LADY OF THE SNOWS.   Oblate Fathers, Pass
Christian, Mississippi 39571 U.S.A. (Roman Catholic--
Oblates of Mary Immaculate) 1953.
Library: 1953, 1, OS, 12,000-12,000, DDC and Peter-
sen, F-S, 150-___, Ar Mi VF   1416

Missouri
OUR LADY OF THE ASSUMPTION ABBEY.   Route 5,
Ava, Missouri 65608 U.S.A. (Roman Catholic--Order
of Cistercians of the Strict Observance) 1950.
Library: 1950, 1, OS, 2,000-1,000, E, A-Z Topi-
cal, 10-___, Ar   1417
MISSOURI SCHOOL OF RELIGION.   9th and Lowry,
Columbia, Missouri 65201 U.S.A. (Independent) 1895.
Library: 1946, 1, OS, 7,000-7,000, E, DDC, F-S,
150-0, VF   1418
CONCEPTION SEMINARY.   Conception, Missouri
64433 U.S.A. (Roman Catholic--Conception Abbey)
1873.
Library: 1873, 2, OB, OS, 100,000-51,000, E,
DDC, F-S, SC, 325-250, Ar Sl Mi Ma VF   1419
MIDWESTERN BAPTIST THEOLOGICAL SEMINARY.
5001 North Oak Street Trafficway, Kansas City,
Missouri 65118 U.S.A. (Southern Baptist) 1958.
Library: 1958, 2, OS, 70,000-50,000, E, DDC,
110-30, Fi Sl Mi VF   1420

NAZARENE THEOLOGICAL SEMINARY.   1700 East
Meyer Boulevard, Kansas City, Missouri   64131
U.S.A. (Church of the Nazarene) 1945.   1421
SAINT PAUL SCHOOL OF THEOLOGY.   5123 Truman
Road, Kansas City, Missouri 65127 U.S.A. (Method-
ist) 1958.
Dana Dawson Library: 1958, 2, OS, 125,000-47,000,
E, LC, 500-___, Sl Mi Mu   1422
WESTERN BAPTIST SEMINARY.   2119 Tracy Avenue,
Kansas City, Missouri 64108 U.S.A. (Missouri Bap-
tist State Convention).   1423
ST. MARY'S SEMINARY.   Perryville, Missouri 63775
U.S.A. (Roman Catholic) 1818.   1424
CARDINAL GLENNON COLLEGE.   5200 Glennon Drive,
St. Louis, Missouri 63119 U.S.A. (Roman Catholic)
1823.   1425
CONCORDIA SEMINARY.   801 DeMun Avenue, St. Louis,
Missouri 63105 U.S.A. (Lutheran Church--Missouri
Synod) 1839.
Library: 1839, 4, OB, OS, 250,000-120,000, E F
G, DDC and LC, SC, 850-___, Ar Sl Mi Ma Mu   1426
COVENANT THEOLOGICAL SEMINARY.   12330 Conway
Road, St. Louis, Missouri 63141 U.S.A. (Reformed
Presbyterian Church--Evangelical Synod) 1956.
Library: 1956, 1, OB, OS, 25,000-16,143, E, LC,
171-7, Fi Sl Pi Ma VF   1427
KENRICK SEMINARY.   7800 Kenrick Road, St. Louis,
Missouri 63108 U.S.A. (Roman Catholic) 1818.   1428
SAINT JOHN'S SEMINARY.   3689 West Pine Boulevard,
Saint Louis, Missouri 63108 U.S.A. (Roman Catholic--
Congregation of the Resurrection) 1918.
Library: 1918, 6, OB, OS, 2,000-2,000, E, DDC,
40-15   1429
ST. LOUIS UNIVERSITY--SCHOOL OF DIVINITY.   Room
0616, 3655 West Pine Boulevard, St. Louis, Missouri
63108 U.S.A. (Independent) 1899.
Library: 1899, 1, OB, OS, 120,000-90,000, E, DDC
and St. Mary College, 800-465, Mi   1430
CENTRAL BIBLE COLLEGE.   3000 North Grant, Spring-
field, Missouri 65802 U.S.A. (Assemblies of God)
1922.
Pearlman Memorial Library: 1922, 2, OB, OS,
50,000-23,000, E, DDC, SC, 243-107, Ar Mi Ma
VF   1431
DRURY SCHOOL OF RELIGION.   1111 North Gladstone
Avenue, Springfield, Missouri 65802 U.S.A. (Chris-
tian Disciples Church) 1955.   1432

Missouri (cont.)

EDEN THEOLOGICAL SEMINARY.   475 East Lockwood,
Webster Groves, Missouri 63119 U.S.A. (United
Church of Christ) 1850.
Library: 1850, 4, OS, 50,000-48,625, E, UTS,
225-200
                                                            1433

Nebraska

CROSIER FATHERS--IMMACULATE CONCEPTION
MONASTERY.   223 East 14th Street, Hastings,
Nebraska 68901 U.S.A. (Roman Catholic--Canons
Regular of the Order of the Holy Cross) 1932.
Library: 1932, 2, OB, OS, 10,000-8,000, E, LC,
F-S, SC, 100-60, Ar Ma Mu VF   1434

New Hampshire

QUEEN OF PEACE MISSION.   Jeffrey Center, New
Hampshire 03454 U.S.A. (Roman Catholic) 1954.   1435
ST. ANSELM'S ABBEY.   College Road, Manchester,
New Hampshire 03102 U.S.A. (Roman Catholic)
1889.
                                                            1436

New Jersey

BLOOMFIELD COLLEGE.   Bloomfield, New Jersey
07003 U.S.A. (Presbyterian Church in the U.S.A.)
1869.
Library: 1869, 4, OB, OS, 65,000-35,000, E, LC,
F-S, SC, 495-350, Ar Mi Pi Ma Mu VF   1437
IMMACULATE CONCEPTION SEMINARY.   Ramsey P.O.,
Darlington, New Jersey 07446 U.S.A. (Roman Catho-
lic) 1860.
                                                            1438
DREW UNIVERSITY.   Madison, New Jersey 07940
U.S.A. (Methodist Church) 1866.
Library: 1866, 12, OB, OS, 400,000-302,000, E G,
DDC and LC, SC, 500-400, Ar Mi VF   1439
ST. MARY'S ABBEY.   Morristown, New Jersey 07960
U.S.A. (Roman Catholic--Order of Saint Benedict)
1929.
Library: 1929, 3, OB, OS, 7,500-5,000, E, St.
John's Union System, 98-90, Ar VF   1440
NEW BRUNSWICK THEOLOGICAL SEMINARY.   21
Seminary Place, New Brunswick, New Jersey 08901
U.S.A. (Reformed Church in America) 1784.
Gardner A. Sage Library: 1784, 3-1/2, OB, OS,
130,000-115,000, E, own, SC, 300-200, Ar Sl Mi   1441
SEVENTH DAY BAPTIST THEOLOGICAL SCHOOL.   510
Watchung Avenue, Plainfield, New Jersey 07060 U.S.A.

(Seventh Day Baptist).

PRINCETON THEOLOGICAL SEMINARY. Box 111, Mercer Street at Library Place, Princeton, New Jersey 08540 U.S.A. (United Presbyterian Church in the U.S.A.) 1812.
Speer Library: 1812, 6, OS, 400,000-282,894, E, LC, SC, 607-379, Ar Sl Mi Pi VF

DARLINGTON SEMINARY. Ramsey, New Jersey 07446 U.S.A. (Roman Catholic) 1860.
Library: 1860, 0, OS, ___-50,000, E, LC, SC, 350-___, Ar Sl Ma

ST. MICHAEL'S PASSIONIST SEMINARY. 1901 West Street, Union City, New Jersey 07087 U.S.A. (Roman Catholic) 1866.

New Mexico
MONTEZUMA SEMINARY. Montezuma, New Mexico 87731 U.S.A. (Roman Catholic--Society of Jesus and Mexican Hierarchy) 1937.
Library: 1937, 2, OS, 45,000-43,000, E F L S, DDC, F-S, SC, 250-170, Ar Mi Ma

New York
ALFRED UNIVERSITY SCHOOL OF THEOLOGY. Box 742, Alfred, New York 14802 U.S.A. (Seventh Day Adventist) 1857.

ST. JOHN VIANNEY SEMINARY. East Aurora, New York 14052 U.S.A. (Roman Catholic) 1961.
Library: 1961, 2, OB, OS, 200,000-30,711, E, LC, 348-211, Fi Sl Mi Ma

MOUNT SAINT ALPHONSUS SEMINARY. Esopus, New York 12429 U.S.A. (Roman Catholic--Redemptorist Fathers) 1907.
Library: 1907, 1, OB, OS, 71,000-42,000, E, LC and Petersen, 362-203, Mi VF

GEORGE MERCER, JR., SCHOOL OF THEOLOGY. 65 Fourth Street, Garden City, New York 11530 U.S.A. (Episcopal) 1955.
Library: 1955, 2, OB, OS, 10,000-10,000 E, DDC, SC, 50-25, Ma VF

CAPUCHIN LIBRARY. Glenclyffe, Garrison, New York 10524 U.S.A. (Roman Catholic--Province of St. Mary of the Capuchin Order).
Library: 1932, 2, OB, OS, 35,000-35,000, E L, DDC, F-S, 200-100, Mi

IMMACULATE HEART OF MARY SEMINARY. Lockland Road, Geneva, New York 14456 U.S.A. (Roman

1442

1443

1444

1445

1446

1447

1448

1449

1450

1451

New York (cont.)
Catholic) 1960.   1452
HOUGHTON COLLEGE.   Houghton, New York 14744
U.S.A. (Wesley Methodist).   1453
BAPTIST BIBLE SEMINARY.   305 Main Street, John-
son City, New York 13790 U.S.A. (General Associ-
ation of Regular Baptist Churches) 1932.
Richard J. Murphy Memorial Library: 1932, 3, OB,
OS, 50,000-30,000, DDC, SC, 360-35, Ar Fi Sl Mi
Pi Ma Mu VF   1454
HOLY TRINITY ORTHODOX SEMINARY.   Jordanville,
New York 13361 U.S.A. (Russian Orthodox Church).   1455
MARYKNOLL SEMINARY.   Maryknoll, New York 10545
U.S.A. (Roman Catholic--Catholic Foreign Mission
Society of America) 1911.
Library: 1912, 6, OB, OS, 45,000-42,728, E, LC
and RC, 540-300   1456
GENERAL THEOLOGICAL SEMINARY.   175 Ninth Ave-
nue, New York, New York 10011 U.S.A. (Protestant
Episcopal Church in the U.S.A.) 1817.
Saint Mark's Library: 1817, 9, OB, OS, 300,000-
150,000, E, DDC, SC, 400-250, Ar Sl Mi Pi Ma
Mu   1457
HEBREW UNION COLLEGE--JEWISH INSTITUTE OF
RELIGION.   40 West 68th Street, New York, New
York 10023 U.S.A. (Jewish) 1922.
Library: 1922, 4, 75,000-86,000, NYPL, SC, 560-
400, Mu VF   1458
JEWISH TEACHERS SEMINARY AND PEOPLE'S UNI-
VERSITY.   515 Park Avenue, New York, New York
10022 U.S.A. (Judaism--Non-denominational) 1965.
Library: 1965, 0, OB, ___-20,000, E Hebrew Yid-
dish, SC   1459
JEWISH THEOLOGICAL SEMINARY OF AMERICA.   3080
Broadway, New York, New York 10027 U.S.A. (Juda-
ism--Conservative) 1890.   1460
LIBRARY OF ST. BEDE.   157 East 72nd Street, New
York, New York 10021 U.S.A. (Anglican) 1937.   1461
NEW YORK THEOLOGICAL SEMINARY.   235 East 49th
Street, New York, New York 10017 U.S.A. (Inde-
pendent) 1900.   1462
RABBI ISAAC ELCHANAN THEOLOGICAL SEMINARY.
186th Street and Amsterdam Avenue, New York, New
York 10033 U.S.A. (Orthodox Jewish).   1463
RELIGIOUS SOCIETY OF FRIENDS.   221 East 15th
Street, New York, New York 10003 U.S.A. (Society
of Friends) 1860.   1464

UNION THEOLOGICAL SEMINARY IN THE CITY OF
  NEW YORK. 3041 Broadway, New York, New York
  10027 U.S.A. (Interdenominational) 1836.
  Library: 1836, 15, OB, 400,000-393,123, UTS,
  SC, 800-500, Ar Mi   1465
UNION THEOLOGICAL SEMINARY IN THE CITY OF
  NEW YORK and AUBURN THEOLOGICAL SEMINARY.
  3041 Broadway, New York, New York 10027 U.S.A.
  (Interdenominational) 1836 and 1818.
  Auburn-Union Lending Library: 1944, 1, OS,
  2,000-2,000, A-Z by author   1466
YESHIVA AND MESIFTA TORAH VODATH. 141 South
  Third Street, Brooklyn, New York, New York 11231
  U.S.A. (Judaism--Orthodox).   1467
YESHIVA RABBI CHAIM BERLIN. 1899 Prospect Place,
  Brooklyn, New York, New York 11233 U.S.A. (Juda-
  ism--Orthodox).   1468
WADHAMS HALL SEMINARY. Riverside Drive, Ogdens-
  burg, New York 13669 U.S.A. (Roman Catholic) 1924.
  Library: 1924, 1, OS, 70,000-35,000, E, DDC, 350-
  300, Sl Mi Mu   1469
ST. ANTHONY-ON-HUDSON. Rensselaer, New York
  12144 U.S.A. (Roman Catholic--Order of Friars Minor
  Conventual) 1912.
  Library: 1912, 2, OB, OS, 46,000-46,001, E, LC,
  F-S, SC, 140-90, VF   1470
COLGATE-ROCHESTER DIVINITY SCHOOL. 1100 South
  Goodman Street, Rochester, New York 14620 U.S.A.
  (American Baptist Convention) 1850.   1471
ST. BERNARD'S SEMINARY. 2260 Lake Avenue, Ro-
  chester, New York 14612 U.S.A. (Roman Catholic)
  1893.
  Library: 1893, 1, OB, OS, 75,000-70,000, E, DDC,
  225-150, Ar Mi VF   1472
CHRIST THE KING SEMINARY. St. Bonaventure, New
  York 14778 U.S.A. (Roman Catholic--Order of Friars
  Minor) 1858.   1473
ST. CHARLES SEMINARY. 209 Flagg Place, Staten Is-
  land, New York 10309 U.S.A. (Roman Catholic--Mis-
  sionary Fathers of St. Charles Borromeo) 1958.
  Library: 1958, 3, OB, OS, 25,000-15,000, E, LC,
  F-S, 210-120   1474
ST. VLADIMIR'S ORTHODOX THEOLOGICAL SEMINARY.
  575 Scarsdale Road, Crestwood, Tuckahoe, New
  York 10707 U.S.A. (Russian Orthodox Greek Catholic
  Church of America--Metropolia) 1938.
  Library: 1938, 2, OB, OS, ___-20,000, E Russian,

New York (cont.)
    own, SC, 100-___, Pi Mu   1475
MOUNT ALVERNIA SEMINARY. Franciscan Friars,
    Wappingers Falls, New York 12590 U.S.A. (Roman
    Catholic--Order of Friars Minor) 1944.
    Library: 1944, 1, OB, OS, 30,000-17,500, E,
    DDC, SC, 173-158, Ar Sl Mi   1476
ST. JOSEPH'S SEMINARY AND COLLEGE. Dunwoodie,
    Yonkers, New York 10704 U.S.A. (Roman Catholic)
    1896.
    Library: 1896, 2, OB, OS, E, LC, SC, 320-165,
    Fi Pi Ma VF   1477
ST. ANTHONY ZACHARIA SEMINARY. Swan Road,
    Lewiston, Youngstown, New York 14174 U.S.A.
    (Roman Catholic) 1960.   1478

North Carolina
BELMONT ABBEY. Belmont, North Carolina 28012
    U.S.A. (Roman Catholic) 1878.   1479
JOHNSON C. SMITH UNIVERSITY. Charlotte, North
    Carolina 28208 U.S.A. (United Presbyterian Church
    in the U.S.A.) 1911.   1480
DUKE UNIVERSITY DIVINITY SCHOOL. Durham, North
    Carolina 27706 U.S.A. (Methodist) 1888.   1481
EVANGELICAL THEOLOGICAL SEMINARY. 2306-08
    East Ash Street, Goldsboro, North Carolina 27530
    U.S.A. (Evangelical Baptists).   1482
HOOD THEOLOGICAL SEMINARY. Salisbury, North
    Carolina 28144 U.S.A. (African Methodist Episcopal
    Zion Church).
    Library: 1, OB, ___-10,529, E, DDC, SC, 88-___,
    Mi Pi Ma Mu VF   1483
SOUTHEASTERN BAPTIST THEOLOGICAL SEMINARY.
    Wake Forest, North Carolina 27602 U.S.A. (Southern
    Baptist) 1951.   1484

Ohio
ASHLAND THEOLOGICAL SEMINARY. 910 Center Street,
    Ashland, Ohio 44805 U.S.A. (Brethren Church) 1930.
    Roger Darling Memorial Library: 1930, 2, OB, OS,
    40,000-25,000, E, UTS, SC, 160-120, Ar Fi Sl VF   1485
ST. JOHN VIANNEY SEMINARY. R.D. 2, Blooming-
    dale, Ohio 43910 U.S.A. (Roman Catholic) 1945.   1486
ST. PAUL MONASTERY. Route 224, Canfield, Ohio
    44406 U.S.A. (Roman Catholic) 1954.   1487
ST. CHARLES SEMINARY. Carthagena Station, Celina,
    Ohio 45822 U.S.A. (Roman Catholic--Society of the

Precious Blood) 1861.
Library: 1861, 1, OB, OS, 60,000-40,000, E,
DDC and Petersen, 355-310, Mi VF   1488
HEBREW UNION COLLEGE--JEWISH INSTITUTE OF
RELIGION.   3101 Clifton Avenue, Cincinnati, Ohio
45237 U.S.A. (Jewish--Reform) 1875.
Klau Library: 1875, 6, OB, OS, 350,000-216,000,
E Hebrew, LC and Freidus, SC, 1,800-1,800, Ar
Fi Sl Mi Pi Ma Mu VF   1489
OUR LADY OF THE FIELDS SEMINARY.   Glendale,
Cincinnati, Ohio 45246 U.S.A. (Roman Catholic--
Glenmary Home Missioners) 1949.   1490
BLESSED SACRAMENT SEMINARY.   5384 Wilson Mills
Road, Cleveland, Ohio 44124 U.S.A. (Roman Catholic--
Blessed Sacrament Fathers) 1934.
Library: 1934, 1, OB, OS, 42,000-25,000, E, DDC
and Walsh, 170-120, Sl Mi Ma Mu VF   1491
ST. MARY'S SEMINARY.   1227 Ansel Road, Cleveland,
Ohio 44108 U.S.A. (Roman Catholic) 1848.   1492
ST. STANISLAUS TERTIANSHIP SEMINARY.   5629 State
Road, Cleveland, Ohio 44134 U.S.A. (Roman Catholic--
Society of Jesus) 1897.
Library: 1897, 1, 15,000-13,600, E, DDC, F-S,
80-63   1493
EVANGELICAL LUTHERAN THEOLOGICAL SEMINARY.
2199 East Main Street, Columbus, Ohio 43209 U.S.A.
(American Lutheran Church) 1830.
Library: 1830, 4, OB, OS, 80,000-40,530, DDC,
338-20, Mi   1494
MARIANIST COLLEGE.   4100 Patterson Road, Dayton,
Ohio 45430 U.S.A. (Roman Catholic--Society of Mary)
1915.
Library: 1915, 1, OB, OS, 50,000-28,000, E L,
DDC, 150-90, Ar   1495
ST. LEONARD COLLEGE.   8100 Clyo Road, Dayton,
Ohio 45459 U.S.A. (Roman Catholic--Franciscan
Fathers of St. John the Baptist) 1868.
Library: 1930, 2, OB, OS, 110,000-36,000, E,
LC and Petersen, F-S, SC, 90-___, Ma Mu   1496
UNITED THEOLOGICAL SEMINARY.   1810 Harvard
Boulevard, Dayton, Ohio 45406 U.S.A. (Evangelical
United Brethren Church) 1873.   1497
METHODIST THEOLOGICAL SCHOOL IN OHIO.   P.O.
Box 364, Delaware, Ohio 43015 U.S.A. (Methodist)
1958.
Library: 1958, 2, OS, 65,000-30,000, E, LC,
185-120, Ar Fi Sl Mi Ma Mu   1498

Ohio (cont.)

WINEBRENNER SEMINARY. 701 East Melrose Avenue, Findlay, Ohio 45480 U.S.A. (Churches of God in North America--Winebrenner) 1942.
Library: 1942, 1, OB, OS, 18,000-8,000, DDC, 91-   1499

DIVINITY SCHOOL OF KENYON COLLEGE. Gambier, Ohio 43022 U.S.A. (Protestant Episcopal Church in the U.S.A.) 1824.
Colburn Library: 1824, 3-1/2, OB, OS, 35,000- 32,831, E, UTS, SC, 196-144, Ar Mi   1500

MOUNT SAINT MARY'S SEMINARY. 5440 Moeller Avenue, Norwood, Ohio 45212 U.S.A. (Roman Catholic) 1831.
Library: 1831, 48, OB, OS, 75,000-54,000, E, DDC, F-S, SC, 322-250, Ar Sl Mi Pi Mu VF   1501

SACRED HEART SEMINARY. Route 1, Shelby, Ohio 44875 U.S.A. (Roman Catholic--Missionaries of the Sacred Heart) 1936.
Library: 1936, 4, OB, OS, 18,000-11,000, E, DDC and Walsh, F-S, SC, 145-75, Ma VF   1502

HAMMA SCHOOL OF THEOLOGY. Springfield, Ohio 45504 U.S.A. (Lutheran Church in America) 1845.
Thomas Library of Wittenberg University: 1845, 2-1/2, OS, 250,000-36,000, E F G, LC, SC, 220-___, Ar Fi Sl Mi Pi Ma Mu VF   1503

OTZER HASFORIM OF THE RABBINICAL COLLEGE OF TELSHE. 28400 Euclid Avenue, Wickliffe, Ohio 44092 U.S.A. (Jewish and Lithuanian Jewish) 1875, 1941.   1504

PAYNE THEOLOGICAL SEMINARY. Wilberforce, Ohio 45384 U.S.A. (African Methodist Episcopal) 1843.   1505

PONTIFICAL COLLEGE JOSEPHINUM. North High Street, Worthington, Ohio 43085 U.S.A. (Roman Catholic--Diocesan Clergy) 1888.
Wehrle Memorial Library: 1888, 1, OB, OS, 60,000- 51,215, E, DDC and Petersen, SC, 317-180, Fi Sl Mi Pi Ma Mu VF   1506

Oklahoma

PHILLIPS UNIVERSITY. Box 2035, University Station, Enid, Oklahoma 73701 U.S.A. (Disciples of Christ) 1907.
Graduate Seminary Library of Phillips University: 1950, 2, OS, 100,000-51,946, E F G, DDC, SC, 423-296, Ar Sl Mi Pi VF   1507

ST. GREGORY'S COLLEGE. Shawnee, Oklahoma

74801 U.S.A. (Roman Catholic--Order of St. Benedict) 1915.
Library: 1915, 2, OS, 30,000-30,000, E, LC, F-S, 264-40 VF
1508

Oregon
TRAPPIST ABBEY. Lafayette, Oregon 97127 U.S.A. (Roman Catholic--Order of Cistercians of the Strict Observance) 1948.
Library: 1948, 2, OS, 12,000-10,000, E, DDC, F-S, 50-20, Sl Mi
1509
WESTERN BAPTIST THEOLOGICAL SEMINARY. 5511 S.E. Hawthorne Boulevard, Portland, Oregon 97215 U.S.A. (Conservative Baptists of America) 1927.
Cline-Tunnell Library: 1927, 2, OS, 40,000-20,000, E, DDC, SC, 350-22, Ar Sl Mi Pi Ma Mu VF
1510
WESTERN EVANGELICAL SEMINARY. 4200 S.E. Jennings Avenue, Portland, Oregon 97222, U.S.A. (Interdenominational) 1947.
George Hallauer Memorial Library: 1947, 1, OS, 40,000-19,000, E, UTS, 115-___, Ar Mi
1511
MOUNT ANGEL SEMINARY. St. Benedict, Oregon 97373 U.S.A. (Roman Catholic) 1889.
1512

Pennsylvania
EASTERN PILGRIM COLLEGE. 1412 East Cedar Street, Allentown, Pennsylvania 18103 U.S.A. (Pilgrim Holiness Church).
Esther G. Hoffman Library.
1513
MORAVIAN THEOLOGICAL SEMINARY. Bethlehem, Pennsylvania 18018 U.S.A. (Moravian) 1807.
Harvey Memorial Library: 1807, 4-1/2, OB, OS, 200,000-20,949, E, DDC, 145-125, Fi Sl Mi
1514
ACADEMY OF THE NEW CHURCH THEOLOGICAL SCHOOL. General Church of the New Jerusalem, 2815 Huntingdon Pike, Bryn Athyn, Pennsylvania 19009 U.S.A. (Swedenborgian) 1876.
1515
CROZER THEOLOGICAL SEMINARY. 21st and Upland Streets, Chester, Pennsylvania 19013 U.S.A. (American Baptist Convention) 1867.
Bucknell Library: 1867, 2, OS, 100,000-87,414, E, DDC, SC, 412-235, Ar Sl Mi Pi Ma Mu VF
1516
ST. PIUS X SEMINARY. Dalton, Pennsylvania 18414 U.S.A. (Roman Catholic) 1962.
Library: 1962, 1, OB, OS, 25,000-9,652, LC, 85-5, Ma VF
1517
LUTHERAN THEOLOGICAL SEMINARY AT GETTYS-

Pennsylvania (cont.)
BURG.   Gettysburg, Pennsylvania 17325 U.S.A.
(Lutheran Church in America) 1826.
Ross Wentz Memorial Library.   1518
KILROE SEMINARY OF THE SACRED HEART. R.D. 1,
Honesdale, Pennsylvania 18431 U.S.A. (Roman Catho-
lic--Society of Jesus) 1955.   1519
CHRIST THE SAVIOUR SEMINARY.   225 Chandler Ave-
nue, Johnstown, Pennsylvania 15906 U.S.A. (Greek
Orthodox: Carpathian, Greek, Russian).   1520
LANCASTER THEOLOGICAL SEMINARY.   West James
and Pine Streets, Lancaster, Pennsylvania 17603
U.S.A. (United Church of Christ) 1825.
Philip Schaff Library: 1825, 5, OB, OS, 150,000-
80,000, E F G L, UTS, 350-250, Ar Fi Sl Mi VF   1521
ST. VINCENT COLLEGE.   Latrobe, Pennsylvania 15650
U.S.A. (Roman Catholic) 1846.
Library: 1846, 6, OB, OS, 400,000-198,895, E L,
LC and Petersen, SC, 910-600, Sl Mi VF   1522
SAINT FRANCIS SEMINARY.   Loretto, Pennsylvania
15940 U.S.A. (Roman Catholic--Friars of the Third
Order Regular of Saint Francis of Penance) 1912.
Library: 1942, 1, OS, 50,000-12,500, E, DDC and
Franciscan, F-S, SC, 150-30, Ar Sl Ma VF   1523
EVANGELICAL CONGREGATIONAL SCHOOL OF THEOL-
OGY.   121 South College Street, Myerstown, Pennsyl-
vania 17067 U.S.A. (Evangelical Congregational Church)
1953.
Library: 1953, 1, OS, 11,000-10,600, E, UTS, 110-
5, Mi   1524
MARY IMMACULATE SEMINARY.   Northampton, Penn-
sylvania 18067 U.S.A. (Roman Catholic) 1939.   1525
ST. CHARLES BORROMEO SEMINARY.   Overbrook,
Pennsylvania 19151 U.S.A. (Roman Catholic) 1832.   1526
EASTERN BAPTIST THEOLOGICAL SEMINARY.   City
Line and Lancaster Avenue, Philadelphia, Pennsyl-
vania 19151 U.S.A. (Baptist) 1925.
Library: 1925, 5, OB, OS, 76,000-67,000, E, DDC,
524-182, Sl Mi Pi Ma Mu VF   1527
FAITH THEOLOGICAL SEMINARY.   920 Spring Avenue,
Elkins Park, Philadelphia, Pennsylvania 19117 U.S.A.
(Independent) 1937.
Library: 1937, 6, OS, ___-22,800, E, UTS, F-S,
125-   , Pi Ma VF   1528
LUTHERAN THEOLOGICAL SEMINARY AT PHILADELPHIA.
7301 Germantown Avenue, Philadelphia, Pennsylvania
19119 U.S.A. (Lutheran Church in America) 1864.

Krauth Memorial Library: 1864, 3, OB, OS,
110,000-92,000, E G, DDC LC Reed, SC, 364-201,
Ar Sl Mi Pi VF   1529
PHILADELPHIA DIVINITY SCHOOL. 4205 Spruce Street,
Philadelphia, Pennsylvania 19104 U.S.A. (Protestant
- Episcopal Church) 1860.
William Bacon Stevens Library and Yarnall Library
of Theology: 1860, 3, OB, OS, 100,000-72,000, E,
DDC, 205-150, Fi   1530
THEOLOGICAL SEMINARY OF THE REFORMED EPISCO-
PAL CHURCH. 25 South 34th Street, Philadelphia,
Pennsylvania 19104 U.S.A. (Reformed Episcopal).   1531
WESTMINSTER THEOLOGICAL SEMINARY. Chestnut
Hill, Philadelphia, Pennsylvania 19118 U.S.A. (Re-
formed Presbyterian) 1929.   1532
BYZANTINE CATHOLIC SEMINARY. 3605 Perrysville
Avenue, Pittsburgh, Pennsylvania 15214 U.S.A. (Byz-
antine Catholic Diocese of Pittsburgh) 1950.
Library: 1950, 3, OB, OS, 4,000-3,000, E, LC,
SC, 83-53, Ar Fi Sl Mi Pi Ma Mu VF   1533
PITTSBURGH THEOLOGICAL SEMINARY. 616 North
Highland Avenue, Pittsburgh, Pennsylvania 15206
U.S.A. (United Presbyterian Church) 1868.   1534
REFORMED PRESBYTERIAN THEOLOGICAL SEMI-
NARY. 7418 Penn Avenue, Pittsburgh, Pennsylvania
15208 U.S.A. (Reformed Presbyterian Church of
North America) 1810.
Library: 1810, 1, OB, OS, 15,000-11,917, E, UTS,
SC, 155-33, Mi Pi   1535
ST. ANN'S PASSIONIST SEMINARY. 1239 St. Ann Street,
Scranton, Pennsylvania 18504 U.S.A. (Roman Catholic)
1906.   1536
SAVANAROLA THEOLOGICAL SEMINARY. 1031 Cedar
Avenue, Scranton, Pennsylvania 18505 U.S.A. (Polish
National Catholic Church).   1537
ST. TIKHON SEMINARY. South Canaan, Pennsylvania
18459 U.S.A. (Greek Orthodox).   1538

Rhode Island
OUR LADY OF PROVIDENCE SEMINARY. Warwick
Neck, Rhode Island 02889 U.S.A. (Roman Catholic)
1939.   1539

South Carolina
CENTRAL WESLEYAN COLLEGE. Wesleyan Station,
Central, South Carolina 29630 U.S.A. (Wesleyan
Methodist) 1906.   1540

South Carolina (cont.)
ALLEN UNIVERSITY--DICKERSON THEOLOGICAL SEMI-
NARY. 1530 Harder Street, Columbia, South Caro-
lina 29204 U. S. A. (African Methodist Episcopal
Church) 1941.
J. S. Flipper Library.   1541
COLUMBIA BIBLE COLLEGE. Box 3122, Columbia,
South Carolina 29203 U. S. A. (Interdenominational)
1923.
Library: 1923, 3, OB, OS, 100,000-25,000, E,
DDC, 360-76, Pi Ma Mu VF   1542
J. J. STARK CENTER OF CHRISTIAN TRAINING.
Columbia, South Carolina 29202 U. S. A. (American
Baptist, National Baptist, Southern Baptist).   1543
LUTHERAN THEOLOGICAL SOUTHERN SEMINARY.
4201 North Main Street, Columbia, South Carolina
29203 U. S. A. (Lutheran Church in America) 1921.   1544
ERSKINE THEOLOGICAL SEMINARY. P. O. Box 267,
Due West, South Carolina 29639 U. S. A. (Associate
Reformed Presbyterian Church) 1837.
Library: 1893, 2, OB, OS, 21,000-19,000, E, DDC,
SC, 208-47, Ar Mi Ma Mu VF   1545
MEPKIN ABBEY. Route 3, Box 222, Moncks Corner,
South Carolina 29461 U. S. A. (Roman Catholic--Order
of Cistercians of the Strict Observance) 1949.
Library: 1949, 1, OB, OS, 15,000-15,000, DDC
and Petersen, F-S, SC, 33-12   1546
MORRIS COLLEGE SCHOOL OF RELIGION. Sumter,
South Carolina 29150 U. S. A. (National Baptist Con-
vention of America).   1547

South Dakota
NORTH AMERICAN BAPTIST SEMINARY. 1605 South
Euclid Avenue, Sioux Falls, South Dakota 57105
U. S. A. (North American Baptist General Conference)
1850.
Kaiser-Ramaker Library: 1948, 1, OB, OS, 35,000-
27,000, E, UTS, 223-___, Sl Mi   1548
WESSINGTON SPRINGS ACADEMY--DEPARTMENT OF
THEOLOGY. Wessington Springs, South Dakota 57382
U. S. A. (Free Methodist).   1549
YANKTON COLLEGE SCHOOL OF THEOLOGY. Yankton,
South Dakota 57078 U. S. A. (Methodist) 1881.   1550

Tennessee
MEMPHIS THEOLOGICAL SEMINARY. 168 East Park-
way South, Memphis, Tennessee 38104 U. S. A. (Cum-

berland Presbyterian Church) 1842.   1551
AMERICAN BAPTIST THEOLOGICAL SEMINARY. 1800
White's Creek Pike, Nashville, Tennessee 37207
U.S.A. (National Baptist Convention, Southern Bap-
tist Convention) 1916.
T. L. Holcomb Library: 1916, 1, 50,000-6,000,
DDC, 50-0, Mu   1552
VANDERBILT UNIVERSITY--DISCIPLES DIVINITY HOUSE.
20th and Adeline Streets, Nashville, Tennessee 37203
U.S.A. (Disciples of Christ).   1553
VANDERBILT UNIVERSITY DIVINITY SCHOOL. Nash-
ville, Tennessee 37203 U.S.A. (Independent) 1875.
Divinity Library of the Joint University Libraries:
1875, 8, OB, OS, 100,000-82,500, E, LC, SC,
327-___, Ar Fi Sl   1554
SCARRITT COLLEGE FOR CHRISTIAN WORKERS. Nine-
teenth and Grand Avenues, Nashville, Tennessee
37203 U.S.A. (Methodist).   1555
UNIVERSITY OF THE SOUTH--SCHOOL OF THEOLOGY.
Sewanee, Tennessee 37375 U.S.A. (Protestant Episco-
pal Church in the U.S.A.) 1878.
Library: 1878, 2, OB, OS, 40,000-39,000, E, DDC,
F-S, 515-336, Ar Sl Mi Mu VF   1556

Texas
AUSTIN PRESBYTERIAN THEOLOGICAL SEMINARY.
100 West 27th Street, Austin, Texas 78705 U.S.A.
(Presbyterian Church in the U.S.) 1884.
Library: 1884, 3, OB, OS, 100,000-79,364, LC,
SC, 644-394, Ar Mi Mu VF   1557
EPISCOPAL THEOLOGICAL SEMINARY OF THE SOUTH-
WEST. P.O. Box 2247, Austin, Texas 78767 U.S.A.
(Protestant Episcopal Church in the U.S.A.) 1951.
Library: 1951, 3, OS, 175,000-42,000, E, UTS,
257-154, Sl Mi VF   1558
BISHOP COLLEGE DIVISION OF RELIGION AND PHI-
LOSOPHY. 3827 Simpson Street Road, Dallas, Texas
75241 U.S.A. (American Baptist Convention, Texas
Baptist Missionary Convention) 1885.
Stanley Kresge Library.   1559
DALLAS THEOLOGICAL SEMINARY AND GRADUATE
SCHOOL OF THEOLOGY. 3909 Swiss Avenue, Dallas,
Texas 75204 U.S.A. (Independent) 1924.
Mosher Library: 1924, 12, OS, 100,000-55,000, E,
UTS, 400-100, Ar Mi Pi Ma Mu VF   1560
PERKINS SCHOOL OF THEOLOGY. Southern Methodist
University, Dallas, Texas 75222 U.S.A. (Methodist)

Texas (cont.)
1915.
Bridwell Library: 1950, 5, OB, OS, 125,000-
104,000, E, DDC, SC, 400-225, Ar Mi VF   1561
ROGER BACON COLLEGE. 2400 Marr Street, El
Paso, Texas 79903 U.S.A. (Roman Catholic) 1940.   1562
ST. ANTHONY'S SEMINARY. Hastings and Crescent
Drive, El Paso, Texas 79903 U.S.A. (Roman Catho-
lic) 1936.   1563
SOUTHWESTERN BAPTIST THEOLOGICAL SEMINARY.
Box 22000, Fort Worth, Texas 76122 U.S.A. (Southern
Baptist) 1908.   1564
TEXAS CHRISTIAN UNIVERSITY--BRITE DIVINITY
SCHOOL. Fort Worth, Texas 76129 U.S.A. (Disciples
of Christ) 1914.
Library: 1914, 2, OB, OS, 160,000-62,092, E, LC,
SC, 556-___, Ar Mi VF   1565
SCOTUS COLLEGE. P.O. Box 85, Hebronville, Texas
78361 U.S.A. (Roman Catholic) 1932.   1566
ST. MARY'S SEMINARY. 9845 Memorial Drive, Hous-
ton, Texas 77204 U.S.A. (Roman Catholic) 1856.   1567
NORTH AMERICAN THEOLOGICAL SEMINARY. P.O.
Box 1288, Jacksonville, Texas 75766 U.S.A. (North
American Baptist Association) 1957.
Kellar Library: 1947, 1, OB, OS, 20,000-5,500,
DDC, 250-30   1568
ASSUMPTION SEMINARY. P.O. Box 28240, 2600 West
Woodlawn, San Antonio, Texas 78228 U.S.A. (Roman
Catholic) 1952.
Library: 1952, 1, OS, 31,800-17,569, E, DDC and
Walsh, F-S, 200-33   1569
OBLATE COLLEGE OF THE SOUTHWEST. 285 Oblate
Drive, San Antonio, Texas 78216 U.S.A. (Roman Cath-
olic--Missionary Oblates of Mary Immaculate) 1927.
Library: 1927, 7, OB, OS, 30,000-21,872, E, DDC
and Walsh, F-S, 265-___   1570
PAUL QUINN COLLEGE AND THEOLOGICAL SCHOOL.
Waco, Texas 76703 U.S.A. (African Methodist Epis-
copal Church).   1571

Utah
ABBEY OF THE HOLY TRINITY. Huntsville, Utah
84317 U.S.A. (Roman Catholic--Order of Cistercians of the Strict Observance) 1947.
Library: 1947, 1, OS, 6,000-3,500, E, 30-25   1572

Vermont
ST. EDMUND'S SEMINARY. Winooski Park, Vermont
05401 U.S.A. (Roman Catholic) 1904.   1573

Virginia
VIRGINIA THEOLOGICAL SEMINARY. 3737 Seminary
Road, Alexandria, Virginia 22304 U.S.A. (Protestant
Episcopal Church in the U.S.A.) 1823.
Library: 1823, 1, OB, OS, 100,000-80,000, E, LC,
F-S, SC, 213-___, Ar Sl Mi   1574
EASTERN MENNONITE COLLEGE. Harrisonburg, Vir-
ginia 22801 U.S.A. (Mennonite) 1917.   1575
VIRGINIA THEOLOGICAL SEMINARY AND COLLEGE.
Lynchburg, Virginia 24205 U.S.A. (Baptist).
Mary Jane Cochlin Library.   1576
UNION THEOLOGICAL SEMINARY IN VIRGINIA. 3401
Brook Road, Richmond, Virginia 23227 U.S.A. (Pres-
byterian) 1867.   1577
VIRGINIA UNION UNIVERSITY. 1500 North Lombardy
Street, Richmond, Virginia 23220 U.S.A. (American
Baptist Convention) 1865.
William J. Clark Library: 1865, 3, OB, OS, 100,000-
70,000, E, DDC, 128-8, Fi Sl Mi Pi VF   1578
HOLY TRINITY MISSION SEMINARY. Box 446, Win-
chester, Virginia 22601 U.S.A. (Roman Catholic)
1954.   1579

Washington
SULPICIAN SEMINARY OF THE NORTHWEST. Kenmore,
Washington 98028 U.S.A. (Roman Catholic) 1931.   1580
MATER CLERI SEMINARY. Spokane, Washington 99228
U.S.A. (Roman Catholic) 1963.   1581

Wisconsin
ST. BENEDICT'S ABBEY. Benet Lake, Wisconsin 53102
U.S.A. (Roman Catholic) 1945.   1582
ST. NORBERT ABBEY. 1016 North Broadway, De Pere,
Wisconsin 54115 U.S.A. (Roman Catholic--Canons
Regular of Premontre) 1898.
Augustine Library: 1898, 1, OB, OS, 12,000-7,000,
E, DDC, F-S, SC, 80-25, Mi Mu VF   1583
XAVERIAN MISSIONARY FATHERS. 6838 South 51st
Street, Franklin, Wisconsin 53132 U.S.A. (Roman
Catholic) 1957.
Library: 1957, 2,000 volumes, LC   1584
THEOLOGATE OF THE PRIESTS OF THE SACRED
HEART. Sacred Heart Monastery, Hales Corners,

Wisconsin (cont.)

Wisconsin 53130 U.S.A. (Roman Catholic--Congregation of the Priests of the Sacred Heart) 1929.
Leo Dehon Library: 1968, 1, OB, OS, 70,000-20,000, E, DDC, F-S, 120-95, Sl Mi Pi Ma Mu VF   1585
CAPUCHIN SEMINARY OF ST. ANTHONY FRIARY. Marathon, Wisconsin 54448 U.S.A. (Roman Catholic) 1918.   1586
WISCONSIN LUTHERAN SEMINARY. 11831 North Seminary Drive, Mequon,Wisconsin 53092 (Wisconsin Lutheran) 1892.   1587
ST. FRANCIS SEMINARY. 3257 South Lake Drive, Milwaukee, Wisconsin 53207 U.S.A. (Roman Catholic) 1856.
Salzmann Library: 1856, 3, OB, OS, 70,000-46,000, E, LC and Petersen, SC, 250-105, Ar Sl Mi Pi Ma VF   1588
NASHOTAH HOUSE. Nashotah, Wisconsin 53058 U.S.A. (Episcopal) 1842.
Library: 1842, 2, OB, OS, 35,000-40,000, E, DDC, F-S, SC, 175-___, Sl   1589
IMMACULATE CONCEPTION COLLEGE. Box 148, Oconomowoc, Wisconsin 53066 U.S.A. (Roman Catholic) 1912.   1590
ST. COLUMBAN'S COLLEGE AND SEMINARY. P.O. Box C, Oconomowoc, Wisconsin 53066 U.S.A. (Roman Catholic--St. Columban's Foreign Mission Society) 1963.
Library: 1963, 1, OB, OS, 25,000-10,000, E, DDC, F-S, 100-80, VF   1591

Oceania

Australia

Australian Capital Territory
ST. MARK'S COLLEGE. Box 67, G. P. O. , Canberra,
A. C. T. , Australia (Church of England in Australia)
1957.
Library: 1957, 2, OS, 100,000-25,000, E, UTS,
70-60, Ar Mi   1592

New South Wales
ST. PATRICK'S ECCLESIASTICAL COLLEGE. Manly,
New South Wales, Australia (Roman Catholic) 1889.
Library: 1834, 1, OB, OS, 75,000-51,500, E, DDC,
SC, 160-102, Ar Sl Mi Ma Mu   1593
ST. JOHN'S COLLEGE. Morpeth, Newcastle, New South
Wales, Australia (Episcopal).   1594
L. A. FALK LIBRARY AND F. L. COHEN MEMORIAL
LIBRARY. 69 Cook Road, Centennial Park, Sydney,
New South Wales, Australia (Jewish) 1920.   1595
MOORE THEOLOGICAL COLLEGE. Newtown, Sydney,
New South Wales, Australia (Anglican).   1596
UNIVERSITY OF SYDNEY--THEOLOGICAL FACULTY.
Sydney, New South Wales, Australia (Independent)
1852.   1597
NEW SOUTH WALES BIBLE COLLEGE. Woolwich, New
South Wales, Australia (Disciples of Christ).   1598

Queensland
PIUS XII REGIONAL SEMINARY. Bariyo, Queensland,
Australia (Roman Catholic).   1599
ST. FRANCIS' COLLEGE. Milton Road, Milton, Bris-
bane, Queensland, Australia (Church of England in
Australia) 1906.
Library: 1906, 1/2, OB, OS, 10,000-6,000, E,
DDC, F-S, 45-32   1600
KENMORE CHRISTIAN COLLEGE. Kenmore, Queens-
land, Australia (Disciples of Christ).   1601
ST. PAUL'S MISSION. Moa Island via Thursday Island,

Queensland (cont.)
Queensland, Australia (Anglican--The Diocese of
Carpentaria in the Church of England in Australia)
1917.
Library: 1917, 0, OS, 750-700, E, F-S, 3-0, Pi
Ma   1602

South Australia
ST. BARNABAS' THEOLOGICAL COLLEGE. Gloucester
Avenue, Belair, South Australia, Australia (Church
of England in Australia) 1880.
Library: 1880, 1, OB, OS, 20,000-11,000, E, DDC,
F-S, 13-___, Ar Fi Sl Mi Pi Ma Mu VF   1603
SOCIETY OF THE SACRED MISSION--AUSTRALIAN
PROVINCE. St. Michael's House, Crafers, South
Australia, Australia (Anglican) 1947.
Library: 1947, 1, OB, OS, 45,000-35,000, E,
DDC, F-S, 37-15, Ma   1604
ST. FRANCIS XAVIER SEMINARY. Rostrevor, South
Australia, Australia (Roman Catholic--Archdiocese of
Adelaide and Diocese of Port Pirie) 1958.
Library: 1961, 1, OB, OS, 12,000-6,800, E F L,
DDC and Walsh, SC, 65-60   1605

Victoria
CORPUS CHRISTI COLLEGE. Glen Waverley, Victoria,
Australia (Roman Catholic--Society of Jesus) 1960.
Library: 1960, 0, OB, OS, 25,000-20,000, E, DDC,
F-S, 50-20, Ma Mu VF   1606
VICTORIA BAPTIST TRAINING INSTITUTE. 152 Water-
dale Road, Ivanhoe, Victoria, Australia (Baptist Union
of Victoria).   1607
COLLEGE OF THE BIBLE. Glen Iris, Melbourne, Vic-
toria, Australia (Disciples of Christ).   1608
MELBOURNE COLLEGE OF DIVINITY. Melbourne, Vic-
toria, Australia, 1853.   1609
PERRY HOUSE. Melbourne, Victoria, Australia (Angli-
can).   1610
QUEEN'S COLLEGE. Parkville N. 2, Melbourne, Victoria, Australia (Methodist).   1611
RIDLEY COLLEGE. Parkville, N. 2, Melbourne, Vic-
toria, Australia (Anglican) 1910.
Library: 1910, 0, OB, OS, ___-6,654, E, UTS,
32-2   1612
TRINITY COLLEGE. Parkville N. 2, Melbourne, Vic-
toria, Australia (Anglican).   1613
BAPTIST COLLEGE OF VICTORIA. 265-9 Errol Street,

North Melbourne, Victoria, Australia (Baptist Union
of Victoria). 1614
ST. COLUMB'S HALL. Wangaratta, Victoria, Australia
(Anglican). 1615

West Australia
WOLLASTON COLLEGE. P. O. Box 36, Claremont,
West Australia, Australia (Church of England in
Australia) 1957.
Library: 1957, 1, OB, OS, 10,000-7,000, E,
Pierce, 9-9, Ma Mu VF 1616

Melanesia

Fiji Islands
METHODIST THEOLOGICAL INSTITUTION. P. O. Box
8, Nausori, Fiji Islands, South Pacific (Methodist)
1912. 1617
PACIFIC THEOLOGICAL COLLEGE. P. O. Box 388,
Suva, Fiji Islands (Independent) 1966.
Library: 1966, 1, OB, OS, 5,000-3,500, E F, DDC,
F-S, 25- 1618
REGIONAL SEMINARY. Suva, Fiji Islands (Roman
Catholic). 1619
ST. JOHN BAPTIST COLLEGE. Box 608, Suva, Fiji
Islands (Anglican--Diocese of Polynesia) 1958.
Library: 1958, 1, OS, 8,000-6,000, E, DDC, 50-0,
Fi Sl Pi Ma Mu VF 1620

New Caledonia
ECOLE PASTORALE DE L'EGLISE EVANGELIQUE.
Bethanie, Chepenehe, Lifou, New Caledonia (Evan-
gelical Church of New Caledonia, Evangelical Mis-
sion of Paris) 1870.
Library: 1960, 0, OB, 1,000-225, F, Subject,
F-S, 5-0, Pi Ma 1621
SEMINAIRE SAINT LEON. Paita, New Caledonia
(Roman Catholic). 1622

New Guinea
NEWTON THEOLOGICAL COLLEGE. Dogura, via Port
Moresby, Papua, New Guinea (Anglican) 1952.
Library: 1952, 0, OB, OS, 7,000-3,000, E, DDC,
F-S, 6-0 1623
SENIOR FLIERL SEMINARY. Logaweng, Finschafen
P. O., Territory of Papua and New Guinea (Evangeli-
cal Lutheran Church of New Guinea, Lutheran Mission

New Guinea (cont.)
New Guinea) 1957.
Library: 1957, 1, OS, 2,000-1,200, E G, DDC,
SC, 10-2, Ma Sl   1624
RARONGO THEOLOGICAL COLLEGE. P.O. Box 90,
Kervat via Rabul, New Guinea (Methodi⁻ᵗ) 1962.   1625
REGIONAL MAJOR SEMINARY. Ulapia, .O. Kokopo,
New Britain, New Guinea (Roman Catholic).   1626
LAWES COLLEGE. Fife Ray, Samarai, Papua, New
Guinea (Papua Ekalesia) 1890.
Library: 1924, 0, OS, 3,000-834, E, Size and
Subject, F-S, 10-0, Sl Ma   1627

New Hebrides
TANGOA TRAINING INSTITUTE. Santo, New Hebrides,
South Pacific (Presbyterian) 1895.   1628

Solomon Islands
ST. PETER'S COLLEGE. Diocese of Melanesia, Siota,
Gela, British Solomon Islands, Pacific (Anglican)
1916.
Library: 1916, 1, OS, 4,000-3,000, D, Accession,
SC, 30-10   1629

Micronesia

Gilbert Islands
TANGINTEBU THEOLOGICAL COLLEGE. Tangintebu,
Tarawa, Gilbert Islands, South Pacific (Congregation-
al) 1961.   1630

New Zealand
COLLEGE OF ST. JOHN THE EVANGELIST. St. John's
Road, Auckland 5, New Zealand (Anglican) 1843.
Kinder Library: 1903, 1, OB, OS, 15,000-12,000,
E, LC, SC, 63-41, Ar Pi Mu VF   1631
CHRISTCHURCH COLLEGE. Box 800, Christchurch, New
Zealand (Anglican).   1632
BIBLE COLLEGE OF NEW ZEALAND. Dunedin, New
Zealand (Disciples of Christ).   1633
PROVINCIAL ECCLESIASTICAL COLLEGE OF HOLY
CROSS COLLEGE. Mosgiel, Dunedin, New Zealand
(Roman Catholic).   1634
SELWYN COLLEGE. 560 Castle Street, Dunedin N. 1,
New Zealand (Anglican).   1635

Polynesia

Cook Islands
TAKAMOA THEOLOGICAL COLLEGE. Box 93, Raro-
toagoa, Cook Islands, South Pacific (Congregational)
1839.   ɪɕɪ   1636
          ꟼ

Samoa
PIULA COLLEGE. Lufilufi, Western Samoa, South
Pacific (Methodist) 1868.   1637
MALUA THEOLOGICAL SEMINARY. Malua, Western
Samoa, South Pacific (Congregational) 1844.   1638

Tahiti
ECOLE PASTORALE D'HERMAN. Box 667, Papeete,
Tahiti, South Pacific (French Polynesian Church,
Reformed) 1870.   1639

Tonga
SIA'ATOUTAI THEOLOGICAL COLLEGE. Box 44,
Nuhu'alofa, Tonga, South Pacific (Free Wesleyan
Church of Tonga) 1948.
Library: 1948, 0, OS, 1,580-1,152, E, Subject,
SC, 8-0, Pi Ma   1640

Tasmania
UNIVERSITY OF TASMANIA--CHRIST COLLEGE. Ho-
bart, Tasmania (Church of England in Tasmania)
1846.
Library: 1846, 1, OB, OS, 10,000-5,000, E, Bliss,
5-2   1641

Argentina
SEMINARIO CONCILIAR. Azul, Argentina (Roman
   Catholic).   1642
COLEGIO SAN JOSE. Ouilmes, Buenos Aires, Argen-
   tina (Roman Catholic).
   Biblioteca "Pio XI."   1643
FACULTAD EVANGELICA DE TEOLOGIA. Camacua
   282, Buenos Aires, Argentina (Disciples, Lutheran,
   Methodist, Presbyterian, Waldensian) 1884.   1644
FACULTAD LUTERANA DE TEOLOGIA. Gaspar Campos
   6151, Jose C. Paz, Prov. Buenos Aires, Argentina
   (Lutheran World Federation, Board of Missions, and
   local churches) 1956.
   Library: 1956, 1, OB, 15,000-12,700, G, UTS, SC,
   120-40, Mu   1645
INSTITUTO BIBLICO BUENOS AIRES. Pampa 2975,
   Buenos Aires 28, Argentina (Christian and Missionary
   Alliance) 1946.   1646
INSTITUTO BIBLICO ESLAVO. Avenida Meeks 860,
   Temperly, Buenos Aires, Argentina (Slavic Gospel
   Association).   1647
PONTIFICIA UNIVERSIDAD CATOLICA ARGENTINA
'SANTA MARIA DE LOS BUENOS AIRES"--FACULTAD
DE TEOLOGIA. Jose Cubas 3543, Buenos Aires 19,
   Argentina (Roman Catholic) 1944.
   Library: 1899, 7, OB, 60,000-35,000, F L, CDU,
   132-100   1648
SALVATION ARMY TRAINING COLLEGE. Tte. Gral.
   Donato Alvarez 465, Buenos Aires, Argentina (Salva-
   tion Army) 1890.
   Library: 1890, 0, OB, OS, 900-665, E S, Subject,
   F-S, 15-3, Ar Ma   1649
SEMINARIO INTERNACIONAL TEOLOGICO BAUTISTA.
   Ramon 1, Falcon 4080, Buenos Aires, Argentina
   (F. M. B. of the Southern Baptist Convention, U. S. A.)
   1912.
   Library: 1952, 2, OB, OS, 25,000-23,000, E S,
   DDC, SC, 150-25, Sl Pi Ma Mu   1650

SEMINARIO METROPOLITANO. Jose Cubas 3543,
Buenos Aires, Argentina (Roman Catholic--Society
of Jesus) 1856. 1651
SEMINARIO RABINICO LATINOAMERICANO. 11 de
Setiembre 1669, Buenos Aires, Argentina (World
Council of Synagogues) 1962.
Library: 1962, 2, OB, OS, 10,000-6,500, E He-
brew S, UTS and Union of Jerusalem, F-S, 24-24 1652
SEMINARIO CONCILIAR. Catamarca, Argentina (Roman
Catholic). 1653
SEMINARIO METROPOLITANO. Avenida V. Sarsfiels
532, Cordoba, Argentina (Roman Catholic). 1654
UNIVERSIDAD CATOLICA DE CORDOBA--School of
Theology. Trejo 323, Cordoba, Argentina (Roman
Catholic) 1956. 1655
INSTITUTO BIBLICO IGLESIA DE DIOS PENA. Casilla
18, Chaco, Argentina (Church of God Mission) 1960. 1656
SEMINARIO "SAGRADO CORAZON." Gandara, Argen-
tina (Roman Catholic). 1657
SEMINARIO METROPOLITANO. Calle 24 entre 65 y
66, La Plata, Argentina (Roman Catholic). 1658
SEMINARIO PIO XII. Mercedes, Argentina (Roman
Catholic). 1659
SEMINARIO METROPOLITANO. Paran, Argentina
(Roman Catholic). 1660
SEMINARIO CONCILIAR. Rio Cuarto, Argentina (Roman
Catholic). 1661
SEMINARIO CONCILIAR. Rasario, Argentino (Roman
Catholic). 1662
COLLEGIUM SANCTI JOSEPHI--COLEGIO MAXIMO.
Avenida Mitre 3226, San Miguel, Argentina (Roman
Catholic--Society of Jesus) 1931. 1663
SEMINARIO METROPOLITANO. Guadalupe-Piedras
7150, Santa Fe, Argentina (Roman Catholic). 1664
UNIVERSIDAD CATOLICA DE SANTA FE--FACULTY
OF THEOLOGY. Saint Martin 1966, Santa Fe, Ar-
gentina (Roman Catholic) 1957. 1665
BIBLIOTECA APOSTOLADO DE LA ORACION. Famailla,
Tucuman, Argentina (Roman Catholic). 1666
SEMINARIO CONCORDIA. Casilla 21, Villa Ballester
F.C.M., Argentina (Lutheran Church of Argentina--
Missouri Synod) 1942. 1667

Bolivia
INSTITUTO BIBLICO "EMAUS." Cajon 514, Cocha-
bamba, Bolivia (Andes Evangelical Mission) 1953.
Library: 1963, 1, OS, 2,500-1,900, S, DDC, F-S,

Bolivia (cont.)
14-4, Pi Ma Mu   1668
SEMINARIO TEOLOGICO BAUTISTA. Casilla 86,
Cochabamba, Bolivia (Canadian Baptist F.M.B.)
1941.
Biblioteca Mable Leaman Smith: 1941, 3, OB, OS,
8,000-5,000, S, DDC, F-S, 15-1, Pi Ma   1669
INSTITUTO BIBLICO DEL BENI. Guayaramerin, El
Beni, Bolivia (Andes Evangelical Mission) 1964.   1670
SEMINARIO MAYOR "SAN JERONIMO." Calle No. 2 y
14 de Septiembre, Casilla 1996, Obrayes-La-Paz,
Bolivia (Roman Catholic).   1671
INSTITUTO BIBLICO BETHESDA. Casilla 290, Santa
Cruz, Bolivia (Evangelical Free Churches--Minne-
apolis) 1962.   1672
SEMINARIO METODISTA WESLEY. Casilla 434, Santa
Cruz, Bolivia (Methodist) 1960.
Felix Olivera Biblioteca: 1960, 2, OS, 4,000-2,000,
DDC, F-S, 15-0, Ma   1673
SEMINARIO TEOLOGICO BAUTISTA DEL ORIENTE
BOLIVIANO. Casilla 181, Avenida 24 Septiembre,
720, Santa Cruz, Bolivia (Junta de Misiones Foraneas
de la Convencion Bautista Brasilera) 1961.
Library: 1965, 2, 5,000-200, Castillian E P, own,
SC, 4-___, Ar Ma Mu   1674
INSTITUTO BIBLICO "SAN JUANILLO." Casilla 201,
Sucre, Bolivia (Andes Evangelical Mission) 1961.   1675
SEMINARIO METROPOLITANO "SAN CRISTOBAL."
Casilla No. 100, Sucre, Bolivia (Roman Catholic).   1676

Brazil
SEMINARIO BIBLICO GOIANO. C.P. 465, Anapolis,
Goias, Brazil (Congregationalist Church of Brazil,
Evangelical Union of South America, Evangelical
United Brethren Church) 1937.   1677
INSTITUTO BIBLICO EVANGELICO EMANUEL. C.P.
10, Aracaju, Sergipe, Brazil (Bethesda Mission)
1964.   1678
INSTITUTO BIBLICO JOAO CALVINO. C.P. 612,
Arapongas, Estado de Parana, Brazil (Presbyterian
Independent of Brazil) 1962.   1679
SEMINARIO TEOLOGICO BATISTA. Caixa 88, Belem,
Para, Brazil (Brazilian Baptist Convention) 1955.
Biblioteca Memorial John S. Oliver: 1960, 1, OB,
OS, 10,000-3,520, P, DDC, F-S, 6-3, Sl Pi VF   1680
SEMINARIO DE INSTITUTO BIBLICO MINEIRO. Belo
Horizonte, Minar, Brazil (Evangelical Union of

South America) 1967. 1681
SEMINARIO MAYOR DE CORACAO EUCARISTICO DE
JESU. Belo Horizonte, Brazil (Roman Catholic). 1682
SEMINARIO TEOLOGICO PRESBITERIANO. Caixa
Postal 133, Campinas, Estado de Sao Paulo,
Brazil (Igreja Presbiteriana do Brasil) 1888.
Biblioteca John M. Kyle: 1888, 2, OB, OS, 16,000-
15,300, E, DDC, 32-0, Ma Mu 1683
BAPTIST BIBLE INSTITUTE. Avenida Silva Jardin 1859,
Caixa Postal 66, Curitiba, Parana, Brazil (South Bra-
zil Mission and the Baptist Convention of Parana) 1940.
Library: 1960, 0, OB, OS, 10,000-2,020, P, DDC,
F-S, 14-6, Ar Sl Pi Ma Mu VF 1684
INSTITUTO TEOLOGICO EVANGELICO. C. P. 2445,
Curitiba, Parana, Brazil (Mennonite Brethren Churches
of South America) 1956.
Library: 1961, 1, OB, OS, 3,000-1,840, G, DDC,
F-S, 22-0, Ma Mu 1685
SEMINARIO MAYOR. Diamantina, Brazil (Roman Catho-
lic). 1686
INSTITUTO BIBLICO DO NORDESTE. C. P. 16, Feira
de Santana, Bahia, Brazil (Baptist) 1946. 1687
SEMINARIO TEOLOGICO BATISTA DO NORDESTE.
C. P. 2, Floriano, Piaui, Brazil (Baptist) 1952. 1688
SEMINARIO MAYOR ARQUIDIOCESANO. Fortaleza,
Brazil (Roman Catholic). 1689
UNIVERSIDADE DO CEARA. Avenida Visconde de Cauipe
2853 CE, Fortaleza, Brazil (Roman Catholic) 1955. 1690
INSTITUTO BIBLICO DA IGREJA DE DEUS. Caixa
Postal 367, Goiania, Goias, Brazil (Church of God)
1964.
Library: 1964, 1, OB, OS, 4,000-768, E P,
Memory-o-matic, F-S, 9-0, Ma 1691
SEMINARIO TEOLOGICO DO RIO DE JANEIRO. Pedra
de Guaratiba, Guanabara ZC 79, Brazil (Congrega-
tionalist, Evangelical Union of South America, Evan-
gelical United Brethren) 1913. 1692
SEMINARIO METROPOLITANO ARQUIDIOCESANO. Joao-
Pessoa, Brazil (Roman Catholic). 1693
SEMINARIO MAIOR DE SAO JOSE. Mariana, Brazil
(Roman Catholic). 1694
INSTITUTO JOAO WESLEY. Rua Sao Vicente 180, Porto
Alegre, Brazil (Methodist Churches of Brazil) 1963. 1695
PONTIFICIA UNIVERSIDADE CATOLICA DO RIO GRANDE
DO SUL. Praca D. Sebastio 2, Porto Alegre, Brazil
(Roman Catholic) 1948. 1696
SEMINARIO CONCORDIA. Rua hucas de Oliveira, 894,

Brazil (cont.)

Porto Alegre, R. G. S. , Brazil (Igreja Evangelica
Luterana do Brasil) 1902.
Library: 1935, 1, OB, 25,000-17,800, E G P,
DDC, F-S, 42-__, Ar Mu   1697
THEOLOGICAL SEMINARY IN BRAZIL. R. G. S. , Porto
Alegre, Brazil (Anglican).   1698
UNIVERSIDADE CATOLICA DO PERNAMBUCO--FACUL-
DADE DE FILOSOFIA. Rua do Principe 526, Recife-
Pernambuco, Brazil (Roman Catholic--Society of
Jesus) 1951.
Library: 1951, 4, OB, OS, 30,000-2,645, P, DDC,
F-S, 135-__, Ar Sl Ma VF   1699
SEMINARIO PRESBITERIANO DO NORTE. C. P. 1751,
Recife, Pernambuco, Brazil (Presbyterian Board of
World Missions) 1924.   1700
SEMINARIO TEOLOGICO BATISTA DO NORTE DO
BRASIL. C. P. 221, Recife, Pernambuco, Brazil
(Baptist) 1902.   1701
INSTITUTO 'SAINT URSULA." Rua Farani 75, Botafogo,
Rio de Janeiro, Brazil (Roman Catholic) 1939.
Biblioteca Santo Augustino.   1702
MOSTEIRO DE SAO BENTO. Ladeira de Sao Bento,
Rio de Janeiro, Brazil (Roman Catholic) 1586.   1703
SEMINARIO MAIOR DE SAO JOSE. Avenida Paulo de
Frontin 568, Rio Comprido, Rio de Janeiro, Brazil
(Roman Catholic).   1704
SEMINARIO TEOLOGICO BATISTA DO SUL DO BRASIL.
Caixa Postal 2541-ZC-00, Rio de Janeiro, GB. , Bra-
zil (Brazilian Baptist Convention) 1907.
Library: 1907, 5, OB, OS, 40,000-13,000, E P,
DDC, F-S, SC, 146-3, Ar Mi Ma Mu VF   1705
INSTITUTO BIBLICO BATISTA INDEPENDENTE. C. P.
172, Rio Grande R. G. S. , Brazil (Baptist) 1953.   1706
SEMINARIO TEOLOGICO BETEL. Rua Figueiras,
Rocha G. B. , Brazil (Independent).   1707
FACULDADE DE TEOLOGIA DA IGREJA METODISTA.
Rua Sacramento 230, C. P. 2, Rudge Ramos, S. P. ,
Brazil (Igreja Metodista do Brasil) 1938.
Library: 1938, 1, OB, OS, 20,000-11,978, E P,
own, F-S, SC, 20-12, Ma Mu   1708
SEMINARIO CENTRAL. Salvador, Brazil (Roman
Catholic).   1709
COLEGIO "CRISTO REI." Sao Leopoldo, Rio Grande
do Sul, Brazil (Roman Catholic--Society of Jesus)
1942.
Library: 1942, 4, OB, OS, __-54,000, G L P,

Subject, F-S, 200-170   1710
IGREJA EVANGELICA DE CONF. LUTERANA BRASIL
(I. E. C. L. B.)--FACULDADE DE TEOLOGIA. C. P.
14, Morro do Espelho, Sao Leopoldo -- RS, Brasil
(I. E. C. L. B. e Ev. Kirche Deutschlande) 1946.
Library: 1959, 1, OB, OS, 25,000-12,000, G, A-Z
by subject, SC, 100-___   1711
ALFONSIANUM. Via Raposo Tavares KN 20, Sao Paulo
9, Caixa Postal 11. 170, Brazil (Roman Catholic--
Congregacao dos Padres Redentoristas) 1936.
Library: 1950, 3, 150,000-52,000, E P, A-Z, SC,
159-___, Ma   1712
THEOLOGICAL SEMINARY OF THE EPISCOPAL
CHURCH OF BRAZIL. Caixa Postal 30. 928, Sao
Paulo, S. P., Brazil (Igreja Episcopal do Brasil)
1903.
Biblioteca Memorial Bispo Thomas: 1903, 2, OB,
OS, 50,000-10,000, E, DDC, F-S, 40-25, Ma   1713
COLEGIO DE CADETES--EXERCITO DE SALVACAO.
Rua Caramuru 931, Sao Paulo, Brazil (Exercito de
Salvacao) 1941.
Library: 1941, 3, OB, OS, 8,000-5,000, S, DDC,
F-S, 15-1, Pi Ma Mu   1714
ESCOLA DOMINICANA DE TEOLOGIA DA PROVINCIA
DOMINICANA BRASILEIRA. Rua Caiubi 126, Sao
Paulo, Brazil (Roman Catholic) 1943.   1715
FACULDADE ADVENTISTA DE TEOLOGIA. C. P. 7258,
Sao Paulo I, S. P., Brazil (Seventh Day Adventist)
1915.   1716
FACULDADE DE TEOLOGIA DA IGREJA METODISTA
LIVRE DO BRASIL. Domingos de Morais 2422, Sao
Paulo 8, G. P., Brazil (Free Methodist Church)
1956.
Library: 1956, 1, OB, OS, 3,500-3,400, E P,
DDC, F-S, 17-3, Sl   1717
FACULDADE DE TEOLOGIA DA IGREJA PRESBITERI-
ANA INDEPENDENTE DO BRASIL. C. P. 300, Sao
Paulo, S. P., Brazil (Presbyterian Church in Brazil)
1905.   1718
FACULDADE TEOLOGICA BATISTA DE SAO PAULO.
C. P. 572, Sao Paulo, S. P., Brazil (Baptist) 1951.   1719
INSTITUTO SALESIANO PIO XI. Rua Pio XI 1024,
Sao Paulo, Brazil (Roman Catholic) 1938.   1720
PONTIFICIA UNIVERSIDADE CATOLICA DO SAO
PAULO--FACULTY OF THEOLOGY. Rua Monte
Alegre 984, Sao Paulo, Brazil (Roman Catholic)
1946.   1721

Brazil (cont.)
SEMINARIO CENTRAL DO IMACULATA CONCEICAO.
Avenida Nazare 993, Ipiranga, Sao Paulo, Brazil
(Roman Catholic).   1722
SEMINARIO MAIOR DO IMACULATA CONCEICAO.
Vianao, Brazil (Roman Catholic).   1723
SEMINARIO TEOLOGICO PRESBITERIANO DO CEN-
TENARIS.   C. P. 855, Vitoria Esp. Santo, Brazil
(Presbyterian Church of Brazil) 1959.   1724

Chile
SEMINARIO CONCILIAR.   Concepcion, Chile (Roman
Catholic).   1725
SEMINARIO MAYOR SAN FIDEL.   Casilla 31, San Jose
de Mariquina, Chile (Roman Catholic--Vicariato
Apostolico de Araucania) 1925.
Library: 1925, 0, OB, OS, 5,000-3,298, S, Series
and Numbers, F-S, 20-0, Ar Ma   1726
COMUNIDAD TEOLOGICA EVANGELICA.   Casilla
14025, Santiago, Chile (Six Protestant denominations)
1964.
Library: 1964, 1, OB, OS, 5,000-2,500, E S, 35-
10   1727
INSTITUTO BIBLICO IGLESIA DE DIOS.   Casilla 10367,
Eduardo Castillo Valasco 520, Santiago, Chile (Church
of God) 1953.
Library: 1953, 0, OS, 1,200-200, S, F-S, 10-__,
Fi Sl   1728
PONTIFICIAL UNIVERSIDAD CATOLICA DE CHILE--
FACULTY OF THEOLOGY.   Avenida Bernardo
O'Higgins 340, Casilla 144-D, Santiago, Chile (Roman
Catholic) 1888.   1729
PONTIFICO SEMINARIO.   Casilla 30D, Santiago, Chile
(Roman Catholic).   1730
SEMINARIO DE LAS ASAMBLEAS DE DIOS.   Casilla
5364, Santiago 3, Chile (Assemblies of God) 1953.
Library: 1953, 1, OB, OS, 2,000-400, S, DDC,
F-S, 6-0   1731
SEMINARIO TEOLOGICO BAUTISTA.   Casilla 9796,
Santiago, Chile (Sociedad Evangelica Bautista y Con-
vencion Evangelica Bautista de Chile) 1939.
Biblioteca Honorio Espinoza: 1931, 1, OS, 8,000-
5,000, S, DDC, F-S, 68-1, Pi   1732

Colombia
SEMINARIO METROPOLITANO.   Barranquilla, Colombia
(Roman Catholic).   1733

SEMINARIO MAYOR. Carrera 7, No. 94-80, Bogota,
Colombia (Roman Catholic) 1948.
Library: 1948, 1, OB, OS, 50,000-15,000, S,
DDC, F-S, SC, 54-54   1734
UNIVERSIDAD JAVERIANA--FACULTADES ECLESI-
ASTICAS. Carrera 10, No. 65-48, Bogota 2, Colom-
bia (Roman Catholic--Society of Jesus) 1938.
Library: 1940, 5, OB, 200,000-110,000, DDC,
F-S, SC, 250-240, VF   1735
SEMINARIO TEOLOGICO BAUTISTA INTERNACIONAL.
Apartado Nacional 779, Cali, Colombia (F.M.B.
Southern Baptist Convention--Richmond, Virginia)
1953.
Library: 1953, 1, OS, 11,000-10,000, E S, DDC,
F-S, 90-75, Ar Sl Pi Ma Mu VF   1736
SEMINARIO METROPOLITANO. Plaza Santo Domingo,
Cartagena, Colombia (Roman Catholic).   1737
SEMINARIO METROPOLITANO. Garzon, Colombia
(Roman Catholic).   1738
SEMINARIO METROPOLITANO. Ibaque, Colombia (Ro-
man Catholic).   1739
SEMINARIO MAYOR DE VOCACIONES TARDIAS. La
Ceja, Colombia (Roman Catholic).   1740
SEMINARIO MAYOR DE MANIZALES. Manizales,
Colombia (Roman Catholic) 1910.
Library: 1910, 2, OB, OS, 25,000-8,000, S, DDC,
F-S, 60-0   1741
SEMINARIO BIBLICO DE COLOMBIA. Apartado Deres
1141, Medellin, Colombia (Christian and Missionary
Alliance, Interamerican Mission Society, L. A. Mis-
sion, Mennonite, Methodist, Presbyterian) 1944.   1742
SEMINARIO METROPOLITANO. La Paz No. 49-44,
Medellin, Colombia (Roman Catholic).   1743
SEMINARIO METROPOLITANO. Nueva Pamplona,
Colombia (Roman Catholic).   1744
SEMINARIO METROPOLITANO. Calle 19, No. 25-78,
Pasto, Colombia (Roman Catholic).   1745
SEMINARIO METROPOLITANO. Popayan, Colombia
(Roman Catholic).   1746
BETHEL BIBLE INSTITUTE. Carrera 22, No. 25-10,
Armenia, Quindio, Colombia (Christian and Missionary
Alliance) 1935.
Library: 1905, 1, OS, 5,000-1,000, S, DDC, F-S,
15-0   1747
SEMINARIO METROPOLITANO. San Gil, Colombia
(Roman Catholic).   1748
SEMINARIO METROPOLITANO. Avenida El Libertador,

Colombia (cont.)
    Santa Marta, Colombia (Roman Catholic).   1749
SEMINARIO METROPOLITANO.   Santa Rosa de Osos,
    Colombia (Roman Catholic).   1750
SEMINARIO METROPOLITANO.   Carrera 3, No. 3-23,
    Tunja, Colombia (Roman Catholic).   1751

Ecuador
ECUADOR BAPTIST THEOLOGICAL INSTITUTE.   Casilla
    3236, Guayaquil, Ecuador (F.M.B. of the Southern
    Baptist Convention) 1960.
    Library: 1960, 1, OB, OS, __-956, A-Z by author,
    F-S, 10-0   1752
SEMINARIO BIBLICO ALIANZA.   Casilla 571, Guaya-
    quil, Ecuador (Christian and Missionary Alliance,
    Evangelical Covenant) 1928.
    Library: 1960.   1753
SEMINARIO MAYOR "SAN JOSE."   Apartado 376, Quito,
    Ecuador (Roman Catholic).   1754

Paraguay
ESCUELA BIBLICA DE LA IGLESIA DE DIOS.   Casilla
    1001, Asuncion, Paraguay (Church of God) 1956.   1755
ESCUELA BIBLICA FILADELFIA.   Casilla 583, Asuncion,
    Paraguay (Philadelphia Evangelicals).   1756
INSTITUTO TEOLOGICO BAUTISTA.   Casilla 989, Asun-
    cion, Paraguay (Baptist) 1956.   1757
SEMINARIO METROPOLITANO.   Calle Pedro Guiggiari,
    entre Mariscal Lopez y Mariscal Estigarvibia, Asun-
    cion, Paraguay (Roman Catholic).   1758
UNIVERSIDAD CATOLICA--LA FACULTAD DE TEOLO-
    GIA.   Asuncion, Paraguay (Roman Catholic--Society
    of Jesus) 1960.   1759

Peru
SEMINARIO MAYOR DE SAN JERONIMO.   Apartado 216,
    Arequipa, Peru (Roman Catholic).   1760
INSTITUTO BIBLICO NAZARENO.   Apartado 420, Chic-
    layo, Peru (Church of the Nazarene) 1921.   1761
COLEGIO UNION--FACULTAD ADVENTISTA DE TEO-
    LOGICA.   Casilla 4896, Lima, Peru (Seventh Day
    Adventist) 1919.   1762
INSTITUTO BIBLICO DE LAS ASAMBLEAS DE DIOS.
    Apartado 4550, Lima, Peru (Assemblies of God)
    1936.   1763
INSTITUTO SUPERIOR DE OBREROS CRISTIANOS DE
    LA IGLESIA METODISTA.   Apartado 1386, Lima,

Peru (Methodist) 1957.   1764
PONTIFICIAL Y CIVIL FACULTAD DE TEOLOGIA.
  Magdalena Vieja, Avenida Sucre 1954, Apartado
  1938, Lima, Peru (Roman Catholic) 1554.   1765
PONTIFICIA UNIVERSIDAD CATOLICA DEL PERU.
  Apartado 1761, Lima, Peru (Roman Catholic) 1917.   1766
SALVATION ARMY TRAINING COLLEGE.   Apartado 1590,
  Lima, Peru (Salvation Army) 1964.   1767
SEMINARIO DE SAN TORIBIO.   Avenida Sucre 1554, Mag-
  dalena del Mar, Lima, Peru (Roman Catholic).   1768
SEMINARIO EVANGELICO DE LIMA.   Apartado 664,
  Lima, Peru (Evangelical Seminary of Lima) 1933.
  Library: 1933, 1, OB, OS, 3,000-2,700, S, DDC,
  F-S, 2-0   1769
INSTITUTO TEOLOGICO BAUTISTA DEL PERU.
  Apartado 572, Trujillo, Peru (Baptist) 1958.   1770

Surinam
MORAVIAN THEOLOGICAL SEMINARY.   Lagweg 4-5,
  Netherlands-Zeist, Surinam (Moravian) 1902.   1771

Uruguay
INSTITUTO TEOLOGICO BAUTISTA DEL URUGUAY. Dr.
  Carlos Martia de Pena 4309, Montevideo, Uruguay
  (Baptist) 1956.
  Library: 1956, 1, OS, 4,000-2,432, S, DDC, F-S,
  2-0, Sl   1772
SEMINARIO EVANGELICO MENONITA DE TEOLOGIA.
  Avenida Millan 4392, Montevideo, Uruguay (Mennonite,
  General Conference Mennonite, Evangelical Mennonite
  Brethren, Menno Mennonite) 1956.
  Library: 1956, 1, OB, 8,000-6,000, S, DDC, SC,
  87-0, VF   1773
SEMINARIO METROPOLITANO INTERDIOCESANO.
  Avenida de las Instrucciones 1115, Montevideo, Uru-
  guay (Roman Catholic).   1774

Venezuela
SEMINARIO DE LA DIVINA PASTORA.   Barquisimeto,
  Venezuela (Roman Catholic).   1775
SEMINARIO INTERDIOCESANO.   San Jose del Avila,
  Apt. 129, Caracas, Venezuela (Roman Catholic--
  Curia Arquidiocesana) 1900.
  Library: 1900, 4, OB, 10,000-5,000, S, DDC,
  F-S   1776
INSTITUTO BIBLICO DE LAS IGLESIAS EVANGELICAS
  LIBRES (I.B.I.E.L.).   Apartado 4713, Maracay,

Venezuela (Independent) 1954.
Library: 1954, 1, OS, 5,000-1,200, E S, DDC
and UTS, 16-16, Ar Fi   1777
SEMINARIO DE LA IMACULADA CONCEPCION.
Merida, Venezuela (Roman Catholic).   1778
SEMINARIO DIOCESANO.   Apartado 26, San Cristobal
(T.) Venezuela (Roman Catholic) 1940.
Library: 1940, 2, OB, 10,000-6,588, F S, DDC
and Cutter, F-S, 35-___   1779

Institution Index

Numbers indicate entries in Geographic Index

Grand Seminaire (Cambrai, France)	611
Grand Seminaire (Chalons, France)	612
Grand Seminaire (Chambery, France)	614
Grand Seminaire (Chartres, France)	615
Grand Seminaire (Coutances, France)	616
Grand Seminaire (Crasville par Evreux, France)	617
Grand Seminaire (Dax, France)	618
Grand Seminaire (Dijon, France)	620
Grand Seminaire (Gap, France)	623
Grand Seminaire (Langres, France)	626
Grand Seminaire (Laval, France)	627
Grand Seminaire (L'Houmeau, France)	630
Grand Seminaire (Le Mans, France)	628
Grand Seminaire (Le Puy, France)	629
Grand Seminaire (Lille, France)	632
Grand Seminaire (Limoges, France)	634
Grand Seminaire (Lucon, France)	636
Grand Seminaire (Marseille, France)	640
Grand Seminaire (Meaux, France)	641
Grand Seminaire (Mende, France)	642
Grand Seminaire (Metz, France)	643
Grand Seminaire (Montauban, France)	644
Grand Seminaire (Montpellier, France)	646
Grand Seminaire (Nantes, France)	648
Grand Seminaire (Nevers, France)	649
Grand Seminaire (Nice, France)	650
Grand Seminaire (Nimes, France)	651
Grand Seminaire (Orleans, France)	652
Grand Seminaire (Pamiers, France)	653
Grand Seminaire (Perigueux, France)	668
Grand Seminaire (Perpignau, France)	669
Grand Seminaire (Poitiers, France)	670
Grand Seminaire (Quimper, France)	671
Grand Seminaire (Reims, France)	672
Grand Seminaire (Rennes, France)	673
Grand Seminaire (Rodez, France)	674
Grand Seminaire (Rouen, France)	675
Grand Seminaire (Saint-Brieuc, France)	676
Grand Seminaire (Saint Die, France)	677
Grand Seminaire (Saint Flour, France)	678
Grand Seminaire (Sees, France)	679
Grand Seminaire (Sens, France)	680
Grand Seminaire (Soissons, France)	681
Grand Seminaire (Strasbourg, France)	684
Grand Seminaire (Tarbes, France)	687
Grand Seminaire (Toulouse, France)	688
Grand Seminaire (Tours, France)	690

St. Charles Seminary (India)   233
St. Charles Seminary (Staten Island, New York,
    U.S.A.)   1474
St. Charles Seminary (Celina, Ohio, U.S.A.)   1488
St. Colomban's Major Seminary   1390
St. Colomban's College and Seminary   1591
St. Columb's Hall   1615
St. Cuthbert's Seminary   545
St. Cyprian's College   149
St. David's College--Bishop Thomas Burgess Theo-
    logical Hall   1132
St. Edmund's College   580
St. Edmund's Seminary   1573
St. Francis Capuchin College   1285
St. Francis' College   1600
Saint Francis Seminary (Loretto, Pennsylvania,
    U.S.A.)   1523
St. Francis Seminary (Milwaukee, Wisconsin, U.S.A.) 1588
St. Francis Seraphic Seminary   1378
St. Francis Xavier Seminary (Australia)   1605
St. Francis Xavier Seminary (Canada)   1169
St. Francis Xavier Seminary (Philippines)   363
St. George's College   282
St. Gregory's College   1508
St. John Baptist College   1620
St. John Fisher and Thomas More Seminary   108
St. John of Rita Theological Seminary   514
St. John Scholasticate   1165
Saint John Vianney Seminary (Rep. of South Africa)   133
St. John Vianney Seminary (East Aurora, New York,
    U.S.A.)   1448
St. John Vianney Seminary (Bloomingdale, Ohio,
    U.S.A.)   1486
St. John's College (Australia)   1594
St. John's College (England)   546
St. John's College (Ireland)   797
St. John's Home Missions   1217
St. John's Seminary (England)   576
St. John's Seminary (India)   202
St. John's Seminary (Camarillo, California, U.S.A.)   1230
St. John's Seminary (Brighton, Massachusetts,
    U.S.A.)   1382
Saint John's Seminary (Plymouth, Michigan, U.S.A.)   1403
Saint John's Seminary (Saint Louis, Missouri, U.S.A.) 1429
St. John's Seminary (Zambia)   174
St. John's University   1406
St. Joseph Cathedral Preparatory Seminary   1363

St. Paul's College (Rep. of South Africa)	124
St. Paul's College (U.S.A.)	1288
St. Paul's Mission	1602
St. Paul's Seminary	154
St. Paul's Theological College	79
St. Paul's United Theological College	56
St. Peter's College (Ireland)	798
St. Peter's College (Rep. of South Africa)	115
St. Peter's College (Scotland)	1027
St. Peter's College (Solomon Islands)	1629
St. Peter's Hall	378
St. Peter's Seminary (India)	236
St. Peter's Seminary (Rep. of South Africa)	125
St. Peter's Seminary "Patriarchal Chaldea"	271
St. Philip's Theological College	148
St. Pius X Seminary (Galt, California, U.S.A.)	1236
St. Pius X Seminary (Dalton, Pennsylvania, U.S.A.)	1517
St. Stanislaus Tertianship Seminary	1493
St. Stephen's College--United Church Theological College	1146
St. Stephen's House	566
St. Sulpice Interdiocesan Seminary	284
St. Theresa Major Seminary	49
St. Thomas More House of Studies	1289
St. Thomas Theological Seminary	1257
St. Tikhon Seminary	1538
St. Vincent College	1522
Saint Vincent Ferrer Seminary	368
St. Vladimir's Orthodox Theological Seminary	1475
SS. Cyril and Methodius Seminary	1402
Salisbury Theological College	573
Salomon Reinach Universite	639
Salvation Army Officers' Training College	328
Salvation Army Training College (Argentina)	1649
Salvation Army Training College (India)	199
Salvation Army Training College (Peru)	1767
Salvation Army Training College for Officers	305
Salvation Army Training Institute	370
Salvation Army Training School	24
S. Agostinio de Macieno	81
S. Francisco de Borja--Facultad Teologica	1042
San Francisco Theological Seminary	1250
San Jose Seminary	376
Santal Theological Seminary	210
Savanarola Theological Seminary	1537
Scarritt College for Christian Workers	1555
Scholasticate Central de Montreal	1186

Seminario de N. S. Da Conceicao   1003
Seminario de Rachal   214
Seminario de San Toribio   1768
Seminario del Vescovile   807
Seminario Diocesano (Italy)   891
Seminario Diocesano (Portugal)   998
Seminario Diocesano (Bilbao, Spain)   1045
Seminario Diocesano (Cadiz, Spain)   1048
Seminario Diocesano (Calahorra, Spain)   1049
Seminario Diocesano (Las Palmas, Spain)   1067
Seminario Diocesano (Orense, Spain)   1073
Seminario Diocesano (Plasencia, Spain)   1079
Seminario Diocesano (Segovia, Spain)   1087
Seminario Diocesano (Siguenza, Spain)   1089
Seminario Diocesano (Tortosa, Spain)   1095
Seminario Diocesano (Tuy, Spain)   1096
Seminario Diocesano (Urgel, Spain)   1097
Seminario Diocesano (Valladolid, Spain)   1099
Seminario Diocesano (Vitoria, Spain)   1100
Seminario Diocesano (Zamora, Spain)   1101
Seminario Diocesano (Venezuela)   1779
Seminario "El Buen Pastor"   410
Seminario Episcopal   993
Seminario Episcopal del Caribe   427
Seminario Evangelico de Lima   1769
Seminario Evangelico de Puerto Rico   428
Seminario Evangelico de Teologia   412
Seminario Evangelico Menonita de Teologia   1773
Seminario Evangelico Presbiteriano   447
Seminario Indigeno del Pilar   47
Seminario Interdiocesano   1776
Seminario Interdiocesano "San Jose"   450
Seminario Internacional Teologico Bautista   1650
Seminario Maggiore (Acireale, Italy)   803
Seminario Maggiore (Acqui, Italy)   804
Seminario Maggiore (Agrigento, Italy)   805
Seminario Maggiore (Alba, Italy)   806
Seminario Maggiore (Aosta, Italy)   810
Seminario Maggiore (Arezzo, Italy)   811
Seminario Maggiore (Ascoli Piceno, Italy)   812
Seminario Maggiore (Bergamo, Italy)   818
Seminario Maggiore (Bielle, Italy)   819
Seminario Maggiore (Bobbio, Italy)   820
Seminario Maggiore (Bordighera, Italy)   822
Seminario Maggiore (Caltagirone, Italy)   825
Seminario Maggiore (Camerino, Italy)   827
Seminario Maggiore (Casale Monferrato, Italy)   829

Seminario Maggiore Arcivescovile--Facolta Teologica
   per l'Aichi Diocesi Napoletana   870
Seminario Maggiore Collegio di S. Bernardino   913
Seminario Maggiore--Como   837
Seminario Maggiore dell'Assunzione   848
Seminario Maggiore della Diocesi di Faenza   627
Seminario Maggiore "San Giovanni Batista"   828
Seminario Maggiore "S. Agata"   830
Seminario Maior (Angola)   4
Seminario Maior (Coimbra, Portugal)   996
Seminario Maior (Guarda, Portugal)   999
Seminario Maior (Lamego, Portugal)   1000
Seminario Maior (Vita Real, Portugal)   1006
Seminario Maior de Branganca   995
Seminario Maior de Cristo Rei (Angola)   6
Seminario Maior de Cristo Rei (Mozambique)   83
Seminario Maior de Imac. Coracao de Maria   1004
Seminario Maior de N. S. da Conceicao   1001
Seminario Maior de N. S. da Purificacao   997
Seminario Maior de Sao Jose (Mariana, Brazil) 1694
Seminario Maior de Sao Jose (Rio de Janeiro, Brazil) 1704
Seminario Maior do Imaculata Conceicao   1723
Seminario Maior N. S. da Esperanca   1005
Seminario Maior Patriarcal de Cristo Rei   1002
Seminario Mayor (Brazil)   .   1686
Seminario Mayor (Colombia)   1734
Seminario Mayor (Albacete, Spain)   1034
Seminario Mayor (Almeria, Spain)   1037
Seminario Mayor (Astorga, Spain)   1038
Seminario Mayor (Caceres, Spain)   1047
Seminario Mayor (Cartagena, Spain)   1050
Seminario Mayor (Ciudad Real, Spain)   1052
Seminario Mayor (El Burgo de Osma, Spain) 1057
Seminario Mayor (Huesca, Spain)   1062
Seminario Mayor (Ibiza, Spain)   1063
Seminario Mayor (Jaca, Spain)   1064
Seminario Mayor (Jaen, Spain)   1065
Seminario Mayor (La Laguna, Spain)   1066
Seminario Mayor (Leon, Spain)   1068
Seminario Mayor (Lerida, Spain)   1069
Seminario Mayor (Orihuela, Spain)   1074
Seminario Mayor (San Sebastian, Spain)   1083
Seminario Mayor (Seville, Spain)   1088
Seminario Mayor (Solsona, Spain)   1090
Seminario Mayor Arquidiocesano   1689
Seminario Mayor de Coracao Eucaristico de Jesu 1682
Seminario Mayor de Manizales   1741

Seminario Teologico Batista		1680
Seminario Teologico Batista do Nordeste		1688
Seminario Teologico Batista do Norte do Brasil		1701
Seminario Teologico Batista do Sul do Brasil		1705
Seminario Teologico Bautista (Bolivia)		1669
Seminario Teologico Bautista (Chile)		1732
Seminario Teologico Bautista de Cuba Occidental		411
Seminario Teologico Bautista de Cuba Oriental		413
Seminario Teologico Bautista de Panama		486
Seminario Teologico Bautista del Oriente Boliviano		1674
Seminario Teologico Bautista Internacional		1736
Seminario Teologico Bautista Mexicano		481
Seminario Teologico Betel		1707
Seminario Teologico Defensores de la Fe		429
Seminario Teologico do Rio de Janeiro		1692
Seminario Teologico Presbiteriano		1683
Seminario Teologico Presbiteriano A. R. de Mexico		475
Seminario Teologico Presbiteriano de Mexico		455
Seminario Teologico Presbiteriano do Centenaris		1724
Seminario Urbano		890
Seminario Vescovile (Alessandria, Italy)		808
Seminario Vescovile (Asti, Italy)		814
Seminario Vescovile (Bagnoregio, Italy)		815
Seminario Vescovile (Caltanissetta, Italy)		826
Seminario Vescovile (Chiavari, Italy)		833
Seminario Vescovile (Chioggia, Italy)		836
Seminario Vescovile (Cremona, Italy)		841
Seminario Vescovile (Lecce, Italy)		859
Seminario Vescovile (Mazara del Vallo, Italy)		863
Seminario Vescovile (Rovigo, Italy)		910
Seminario Vescovile (Senigallia, Italy)		916
Seminario Vescovile di Feltre		846
Seminario Vescovile di Novara		875
Seminario Vescovile di Trieste		924
Seminario Vescovile "Santangelo"		823
Seminarium Duchowne (Bialystok, Poland)		965
Seminarium Duchowne (Drohiczyn, Poland)		966
Seminarium Duchowne (Gdansk, Poland)		967
Seminarium Duchowne (Gniezno, Poland)		968
Seminarium Duchowne (Gorzoro, Poland)		969
Seminarium Duchowne (Kielce, Poland)		970
Seminarium Duchowne (Krakow, Poland)		971
Seminarium Duchowne (Lodz, Poland)		974
Seminarium Duchowne (Lomza, Poland)		975
Seminarium Duchowne (Lubaczow, Poland)		976
Seminarium Duchowne (Lubin, Poland)		978
Seminarium Duchowne (Olsztyn, Poland)		979

Religious Group Index

Numbers indicate entries in Geographic Index

Advent Christian Church 1387
African Inland Mission 18, 57
Andes Evangelical Mission 1668, 1670, 1675
Anglican 7, 8, 56, 60, 65, 67, 77, 79, 81, 99, 102, 110,
114, 115, 117, 118, 120, 124, 144, 148, 149, 159, 164,
165, 171, 174, 179, 180, 185, 188, 198, 203, 208, 211,
220, 235, 282, 290, 297, 304, 343, 351, 356, 369, 378,
379, 396, 409, 412, 418, 427, 440, 470, 526, 529, 530,
533, 536, 538, 539, 540, 541, 542, 543, 544, 548, 549,
550, 552, 554, 561, 562, 565, 566, 571, 572, 573, 574,
581, 582, 584, 1028, 1029, 1129, 1132, 1147, 1149,
1150, 1154, 1159, 1160, 1175, 1176, 1178, 1212, 1223,
1227, 1239, 1262, 1318, 1355, 1384, 1386, 1450, 1457,
1461, 1500, 1530, 1556, 1558, 1574, 1589, 1592, 1594,
1596, 1600, 1602, 1603, 1604, 1610, 1612, 1613, 1615,
1616, 1620, 1623, 1629, 1631, 1632, 1635, 1641, 1698,
1713
Assemblies of God 237, 296, 1431, 1731, 1763

Baptist 12, 16, 22, 23, 33, 48, 52, 84, 95, 97, 105, 119,
146, 175, 176, 177, 181, 188, 190, 195, 200, 203, 204,
207, 242, 246, 266, 285, 294, 311, 335, 340, 353, 355,
360, 367, 390, 399, 403, 408, 411, 413, 416, 419, 437,
446, 448, 451, 479, 481, 484, 486, 524, 534, 568, 780,
1124, 1128, 1130, 1139, 1145, 1155, 1157, 1221, 1222,
1232, 1233, 1243, 1246, 1254, 1301, 1315, 1324, 1340,
1353, 1358, 1359, 1364, 1393, 1409, 1411, 1420, 1423,
1442, 1454, 1471, 1482, 1484, 1510, 1516, 1527, 1543,
1547, 1548, 1552, 1559, 1564, 1568, 1576, 1578, 1607,
1614, 1650, 1669, 1674, 1680, 1684, 1687, 1688, 1701,
1705, 1706, 1719, 1736, 1752, 1757, 1770, 1772

Christian and Missionary Alliance 189, 287, 380, 381, 385,
1646, 1742, 1747, 1753
Christian Churches (includes Disciples) 23, 27, 59, 298,
322, 329, 362, 468, 1221, 1231, 1263, 1308, 1341, 1346,

215

Presbyterian (all branches) 10, 13, 14, 23, 26, 27, 50,
56, 62, 78, 99, 114, 144, 205, 206, 221, 235, 313, 315,
316, 323, 326, 330, 333, 334, 337, 343, 356, 362, 364,
379, 391, 402, 412, 434, 447, 455, 475, 801, 1026,
1030, 1033, 1126, 1171, 1185, 1221, 1303, 1311, 1348,
1357, 1427, 1437, 1443, 1480, 1532, 1534, 1535, 1545,
1551, 1557, 1577, 1628, 1644, 1681, 1683, 1700, 1718,
1724, 1742
Protestant 657, 658, 732, 788, 1116
Protestant Church of Timur 259
Protestant Churches of Central and Eastern Java 255
Protestant Council 38

Reformed 12, 36, 40, 62, 68, 82, 106, 116, 128, 129,
130, 134, 137, 139, 140, 144, 172, 187, 197, 220, 240,
255, 260, 289, 397, 518, 645, 683, 784, 785, 787, 988,
1011, 1106, 1114, 1119, 1125, 1401, 1441, 1639
Reformed Episcopal 1531
Roman Catholic 1, 2, 4, 6, 17, 19, 25, 28, 29, 31, 32,
35, 39, 44, 45, 47, 49, 53, 54, 61, 63, 64, 74, 76,
83, 88, 90, 98, 101, 108, 111, 125, 133, 145, 147, 150,
151, 153, 154, 156, 158, 161, 163, 169, 182, 183, 186,
194, 202, 213, 214, 215, 217, 226, 227, 231, 233, 234,
236, 241, 245, 247, 248, 252, 253, 258, 261, 262, 264,
268, 271, 272, 276, 280, 281, 283, 284, 302, 303, 327,
344, 345, 346, 347, 350, 352, 357, 358, 361, 363, 366,
368, 371, 373, 374, 375, 376, 377, 382, 383, 384, 386,
387, 388, 410, 414, 417, 426, 429, 431, 439, 441, 450,
452, 453, 454, 456, 457, 458, 460, 461, 462, 463, 464,
465, 466, 469, 471, 472, 473, 474, 476, 477, 478, 480,
482, 485, 488, 489, 490, 491, 492, 493, 494, 495, 499,
500, 501, 502, 503, 504, 505, 506, 507, 508, 509, 510,
511, 512, 513, 545, 547, 567, 569, 570, 576, 578, 579,
580, 583, 588, 589, 590, 591, 593, 594, 595, 596, 597,
598, 599, 600, 601, 602, 603, 604, 605, 606, 607, 608,
609, 610, 611, 612, 613, 614, 615, 616, 617, 618, 619,
620, 621, 622, 623, 624, 625, 626, 627, 628, 629, 630,
631, 632, 633, 634, 635, 636, 637, 638, 639, 640, 641,
642, 643, 644, 646, 647, 648, 649, 650, 651, 652, 653,
656, 659, 660, 663, 664, 666, 667, 668, 669, 670, 671,
672, 673, 674, 675, 676, 677, 678, 679, 680, 681, 682,
684, 685, 686, 687, 688, 689, 690, 691, 692, 693, 694,
695, 696, 697, 698, 699, 701, 705, 707, 711, 712, 714,
715, 721, 722, 723, 724, 725, 731, 734, 735, 736, 739,
740, 741, 745, 746, 747, 749, 750, 751, 752, 753, 756,
757, 758, 759, 760, 764, 765, 771, 774, 781, 789, 790,
791, 794, 795, 796, 797, 798, 802, 803, 804, 805, 806,

807, 808, 809, 810, 811, 812, 813, 814, 815, 816, 817,
818, 819, 820, 821, 822, 823, 824, 825, 826, 827, 828,
829, 830, 831, 832, 833, 834, 835, 836, 837, 838, 839,
841, 842, 843, 844, 845, 846, 847, 848, 849, 850, 851,
852, 853, 854, 855, 856, 857, 858, 859, 860, 861, 862,
863, 864, 865, 866, 867, 868, 869, 870, 871, 872, 873,
874, 875, 876, 877, 878, 879, 880, 881, 882, 883, 884,
885, 886, 887, 888, 889, 890, 891, 892, 893, 894, 895,
896, 897, 898, 899, 900, 901, 902, 903, 904, 905, 906,
907, 908, 909, 910, 911, 912, 913, 914, 915, 916, 917,
918, 919, 920, 921, 922, 923, 924, 925, 926, 927, 928,
929, 930, 931, 932, 933, 934, 935, 936, 937, 941, 945,
946, 947, 949, 950, 951, 952, 954, 955, 956, 958, 959,
961, 965, 966, 967, 968, 969, 970, 971, 972, 973, 974,
975, 976, 977, 978, 979, 980, 981, 982, 983, 984, 985,
986, 988, 990, 991, 992, 993, 994, 995, 996, 997, 998,
999, 1000, 1001, 1002, 1003, 1004, 1005, 1006, 1027,
1032, 1034, 1035, 1036, 1037, 1038, 1039, 1040, 1041,
1042, 1043, 1044, 1045, 1046, 1047, 1048, 1049, 1050,
1051, 1052, 1053, 1054, 1055, 1056, 1057, 1058, 1059,
1060, 1061, 1062, 1063, 1064, 1065, 1066, 1067, 1068,
1069, 1070, 1071, 1072, 1073, 1074, 1075, 1076, 1077,
1078, 1079, 1080, 1081, 1082, 1083, 1084, 1085, 1086,
1087, 1088, 1089, 1090, 1091, 1092, 1093, 1094, 1095,
1096, 1097, 1098, 1099, 1100, 1101, 1102, 1107, 1109,
1111, 1112, 1113, 1117, 1118, 1120, 1121, 1122, 1136,
1138, 1140, 1143, 1144, 1151, 1153, 1156, 1161, 1162,
1163, 1164, 1165, 1166, 1167, 1168, 1169, 1172, 1173,
1174, 1179, 1181, 1182, 1183, 1186, 1187, 1188, 1189,
1190, 1191, 1192, 1194, 1195, 1196, 1197, 1198, 1199,
1200, 1201, 1202, 1203, 1204, 1205, 1206, 1207, 1208,
1209, 1210, 1211, 1215, 1217, 1218, 1219, 1220, 1221,
1229, 1230, 1235, 1236, 1244, 1245, 1247, 1251, 1252,
1253, 1256, 1257, 1258, 1260, 1265, 1266, 1267, 1268,
1269, 1270, 1271, 1272, 1273, 1274, 1275, 1277, 1278,
1279, 1280, 1281, 1282, 1283, 1284, 1285, 1286, 1287,
1288, 1289, 1290, 1291, 1292, 1293, 1295, 1296, 1298,
1305, 1319, 1320, 1322, 1325, 1326, 1327, 1330, 1331,
1332, 1334, 1336, 1339, 1343, 1344, 1347, 1349, 1350,
1352, 1354, 1360, 1361, 1363, 1365, 1368, 1370, 1371,
1372, 1373, 1374, 1375, 1376, 1377, 1378, 1382, 1389,
1390, 1391, 1394, 1395, 1397, 1398, 1402, 1403, 1404,
1405, 1406, 1414, 1415, 1416, 1417, 1419, 1424, 1425,
1428, 1429, 1434, 1435, 1436, 1438, 1440, 1444, 1445,
1446, 1448, 1449, 1451, 1452, 1456, 1469, 1470, 1472,
1473, 1474, 1476, 1477, 1478, 1479, 1486, 1487, 1488,
1490, 1491, 1492, 1493, 1495, 1501, 1502, 1506, 1508,

Roman Catholic (cont.)
    1509, 1512, 1517, 1519, 1522, 1523, 1525, 1526, 1533,
    1536, 1537, 1539, 1546, 1549, 1550, 1562, 1563, 1566,
    1567, 1569, 1570, 1572, 1573, 1579, 1580, 1581, 1582,
    1583, 1584, 1585, 1586, 1588, 1590, 1591, 1593, 1599,
    1605, 1606, 1619, 1622, 1626, 1634, 1642, 1643, 1648,
    1651, 1653, 1654, 1655, 1657, 1658, 1659, 1660, 1661,
    1662, 1663, 1664, 1665, 1666, 1671, 1676, 1682, 1686,
    1689, 1690, 1693, 1694, 1696, 1699, 1702, 1703, 1704,
    1709, 1710, 1711, 1715, 1720, 1721, 1722, 1723, 1725,
    1726, 1729, 1730, 1732, 1733, 1734, 1735, 1737, 1738,
    1739, 1740, 1741, 1743, 1744, 1745, 1746, 1747, 1749,
    1750, 1751, 1754, 1758, 1759, 1760, 1765, 1766, 1768,
    1774, 1775, 1776, 1778, 1779

Salvation Army   24, 104, 126, 184, 199, 305, 328, 370,
    1649, 1714, 1767
Seventh Day Adventist   103, 160, 324, 400, 423, 432, 1238,
    1304, 1399, 1447, 1716, 1762
Slavic Gospel Association   1647
Society of Friends   69, 70, 444, 551, 1342, 1464
South China Island Union   400
Sudan United Mission   89
Swedenborgian   1381, 1392, 1515

True Jesus Church   395

Unevangelized Field Mission   18
Union Church of North Madagascar   69
Unitarian   1221, 1312, 1388
United Brethren in Christ   113, 1338
United Church of Canada   3, 221, 321, 1146, 1148, 1152,
    1158, 1170, 1180, 1193, 1214
United Church of Christ   3, 260, 364, 449, 1221, 1306,
    1366, 1410, 1433, 1521
United Church of Christ in Japan   310
United Church of Christ in the Philippines   362, 365
United Church of North India   216, 221, 235, 246
United Church of Pakistan   356
United Church of Zambia   173
United Missionary Society of Elkhart, Indiana   94
Universalist   1312, 1388

Waldensian   1644
World Council of Churches   1115